small HOME PLANS

Small Home Plans is a collection of our best-selling small homes in a variety of styles. These plans cover a wide range of architectural styles. A broad assortment is presented to match a wide variety of lifestyles and budgets. Each design page features floor plans, a front view of the house, interior square footage of the home, number of bedrooms, baths, garage size and foundation types. All floor plans show room and exterior dimensions.

Technical Specifications

At the time the construction drawings were prepared, every effort was made to ensure that these plans and specifications meet nationally recognized building codes (BOCA, Southern Building Code Congress and others). Because national building codes change or vary from area to area some drawing modifications and/or the assistance of a professional designer or architect may be necessary to comply with your local codes or to accommodate specific building site conditions. We advise you to consult with your local building official for information regarding codes governing your area.

Blueprint Ordering - Fast and Easy

Your ordering is made simple by following the instructions on page 7. See page 6 for more information on which types of blueprint packages are available and how many plan sets to order.

Your Home, Your Way

The blueprints you receive are a master plan for building your new home. They start you on your way to what may well be the most rewarding experience of your life.

CONTENTS

"Thanks to **MENARDS**®, finding and building our Dream Home has never been easier."

Thinking about building your dream home? Or, perhaps you are interested in a vacation home or downsizing to a single story home? Choosing a home plan can be a daunting task.

This book of Small Home Plans including best-selling Multi-Family plans has been designed to make the search simple and easy. Browse the pages of this book and look for the style that best suits your family and your needs. These plans have been chosen from top designers from across the country and can provide to you the perfect home that will truly be a place of refuge for your whole family for years to come.

This book is the perfect place to begin your search for the home of your dreams. You will find the expected beauty you want and the functional efficiency you need, all designed with unmatched quality.

Also, keep in mind, this book contains helpful articles for understanding what kind of plan package you may need as well as other helpful building aids to make the process even easier.

When you have made this decision visit your local **MENARDS**® store to place your order and partner with one of their friendly team members to walk you through the process.

MENARDS® is dedicated to assist you through the entire home decision process.

What's The Right Plan For You?

Choosing a home plan is an exciting but difficult task. Many factors play a role in what home plan is best for you and your family. To help you get started, we have pinpointed some of the major factors to consider when searching for your dream home. Take the time to evaluate your family's needs and you will have an easier time sorting through all of the home plans offered in this book.

Budget: The first thing to consider is your budget. Many items take part in this budget, from ordering the blueprints to the last doorknob purchased. Once you have found your dream home plan, visit the **MENARDS**® Building Materials Desk to get a cost-to-build estimate to ensure that the finished product is still within your price range.

Family Lifestyle: After your budget is deciphered, you need to assess you and your family's lifestyle needs. Think about the stage of life you are at now, and what stages you will be going through in the future. Ask yourself questions to figure out how much room you need now and if you will need room for expansion. Are you married? Do you have children? How many children do you plan on having? Are you an empty-nester?

Incorporate in your planning any frequent guests you may have, including elderly parents, grandchildren or adult children who may live with you.

Does your family entertain a lot? If so, think about the rooms you will need to do so. Will you need both formal and informal spaces? Do you need a gourmet kitchen? Do you need a game room and/or a wet bar?

> Experts in the field suggest that the best way to determine your needs is to begin by listing everything you like or dislike about your current home.

Floor Plan Layouts: When looking through our home plans, imagine yourself walking through the house. Consider the flow from the entry to the living, sleeping and gathering areas. Does the layout ensure privacy for the master bedroom? Does the garage enter near the kitchen for easy unloading? Does the placement of the windows provide enough privacy from any neighboring properties? Do you plan on using furniture you already have? Will this furniture fit in the appropriate rooms? When you find a plan you want to purchase, be sure to picture yourself actually living in it.

Exterior Spaces: There are many different home styles ranging from Traditional to Contemporary. Flip through and find which style most appeals to you and the neighborhood in which you plan to build. Also think of your site and how the entire house will fit on this site. Picture any landscaping you plan on incorporating into the design. Using your imagination is key when choosing a home plan.

Choosing a home plan can be an intimidating experience. Asking yourself these questions before you get started on the search will help you through the process. With our large selection of multiple styles we are certain you will find your dream home in the following pages.

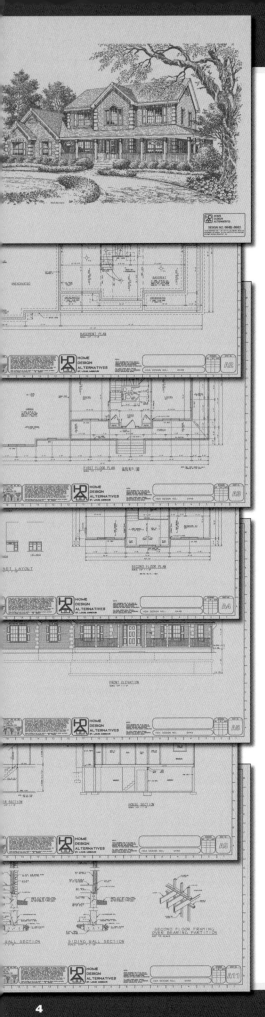

Quality plans for building your future, with extras that provide unsurpassed value, ensure good construction and long-term enjoyment.

1. Cover Sheet

Included with many of the plans, the cover sheet is the artist's rendering of the exterior of the home. It will give you an idea of how your home will look when completed and landscaped.

2. Foundation

The foundation plan shows the layout of the basement, walk-out basement, crawl space, slab or pier foundation. All necessary notations and dimensions are included. See plan page for the foundation types included. If the home plan you choose does not have your desired foundation type, call or visit any **MENARDS** and they can advise you on how to customize your foundation to suit your specific needs or site conditions.

3. Floor Plans

The floor plans show the placement of walls, doors, closets, plumbing fixtures, electrical outlets, columns, and beams for each level of the home.

4. Interior Elevations

Interior elevations provide views of special interior elements such as fireplaces, kitchen cabinets, built-in units and other features of the home.

5. Exterior Elevations

Exterior elevations illustrate the front, rear and both sides of the house, with all details of exterior materials and the required dimensions.

6. Sections

Show detail views of the home or portions of the home as if it were sliced from the roof to the foundation. This sheet shows important areas such as load-bearing walls, stairs, joists, trusses and other structural elements, which are critical for proper construction.

7. Details

Show how to construct certain components of your home, such as the roof system, stairs, deck, etc.

Your Blueprint Package will contain the necessary construction information to build your home. We also offer the following products and services to save you time and money in the building process.

Material List

Material lists are available for all the plans in this book. Each list gives you the quantity, dimensions and description of the building materials necessary to construct your home. You'll get faster and more accurate bids from your contractor while saving money by paying for only the materials you need. To receive a free home plan estimate call or visit any **MENARDS** Building Materials Desk.

Discount Price: $125.00 - Menards SKU 100-3422
Note: Material lists are not refundable.

Express Delivery

Most orders are processed within 24 hours of receipt. Please allow 7-10 business days for delivery. If you need to place a rush order, please call or visit any **MENARDS** store to order by 11:00 a.m. Monday-Friday CST and specify you would like express service (allow 1-2 business days.

Discount Price: $40.00
Menards SKU 194-4356

Technical Assistance

If you have additional questions, call our technical support line at 1-314-770-2228 between 8:00 a.m. and 5:00 p.m. Monday-Friday CST. Whether it involves design modifications or field assistance, our designers are extremely familiar with all of our designs and will be happy to help you. We want your home to be everything you expect it to be.

Other Great Products . . .

The Legal Kit

Avoid many legal pitfalls and build your home with confidence using the forms and contracts featured in this kit. Included are request for proposal documents, various fixed price and cost plus contracts, instructions on how and when to use each form, warranty statements and more. Save time and money before you break ground on your new home or start a remodeling project. All forms are reproducible. The kit is ideal for homebuilders and contractors.

Discount Price: $35.00 - Menards SKU 100-3422

Detail Plan Packages - Electrical, Plumbing & Framing Packages

Three separate packages offer homebuilders details for constructing various foundations; numerous floor, wall and roof framing techniques; simple to complex residential wiring; sump pump and water softener hookups; plumbing connection methods; installation of septic systems, and more. Each package includes three dimensional illustrations and a glossary of terms. Purchase one or all three. Note: These drawings do not pertain to a specific home plan.

Discount Price: $20.00 each or all three for $40.00
Menards SKU 100-3422

Now that you've found the home you've been looking for, here are some suggestions on how to make your Dream Home a reality. To get started, order the type of plans that fit your particular situation.

Your Choices

The One-Set Study Package*

We offer a One-set plan package so you can study your home in detail. This one set is considered a study set and is marked "not for construction." It is a copyright violation to reproduce blueprints.

The Minimum 5-Set Package*

If you're ready to start the construction process, this 5-Set package is the minimum number of blueprint sets you will need. It will require keeping close track of each set so they can be used by multiple subcontractors and tradespeople.

The Standard 8-Set Package*

For best results in terms of cost, schedule and quality of construction, we recommend you order eight (or more) sets of blueprints. Besides one set for yourself, additional sets of blueprints will be required by your mortgage lender, local building department, general contractor and all subcontractors working on foundation, electrical, plumbing, heating/air conditioning, carpentry work, etc.

Reproducible Masters

If you wish to make some minor design changes, you'll want to order reproducible masters. These drawings

contain the same information as the blueprints but are printed on reproducible paper that is easy to alter and clearly indicates your right to copy or reproduce. This will allow your builder or a local design professional to make the necessary drawing changes without the major expense of redrawing the plans. This package also allows you to print copies of the modified plans as needed. The right of building only one structure from these plans is licensed exclusively to the buyer. You may not use this design to build a second or multiple dwelling(s) without purchasing another blueprint. Each violation of the Copyright Law is punishable in a fine.

Mirror Reverse Sets

Plans can be printed in mirror reverse. These plans are useful when the house would fit your site better if all the rooms were on the opposite side than shown. They are simply a mirror image of the original drawings causing the lettering and dimensions to read backwards. Therefore, when ordering mirror reverse drawings, you must purchase at least one set of right-reading plans.

* Additional sets of the same plan ordered are available only within 90 days after purchase of original plan package.

Discount Price: $45.00 - Menards SKU 194-4330

You've found your Dream Home, now what?

Follow these simple steps

1. Review the article on page 6 to decide what type of plan package you need.

2. To order, call or visit any **MENARDS**® store and go to the Building Materials Desk.

To locate the **MENARDS**® store nearest you go to **www.Menards.com**, click on Store Service then click on the Store locator.

Artist drawings and photos shown in this publication may vary slightly from the actual working drawings. Some photos are shown in mirror reverse. Please refer to the floor plan for accurate layout.

BLUEPRINT SKU PRICING

PRICE CODE		1-SET STUDY	5-SET PLAN	8-SET PLAN	REPRO. MASTERS
AAA	Menards SKU	194-3920	194-3933	194-3946	194-3959
	Discount Price	$310	$380	$425	$525
AA	Menards SKU	194-3962	194-3975	194-3988	194-3991
	Discount Price	$410	$480	$525	$625
A	Menards SKU	194-4000	194-4084	194-4165	194-4246
	Discount Price	$470	$540	$585	$686
B	Menards SKU	194-4013	194-4097	194-4178	194-4259
	Discount Price	$530	$600	$645	$745
C	Menards SKU	194-4026	194-4107	194-4181	194-4262
	Discount Price	$585	$655	$700	$800
D	Menards SKU	194-4039	194-4110	194-4194	194-4275
	Discount Price	$635	$705	$750	$850
E	Menards SKU	194-4042	194-4123	194-4204	194-4288
	Discount Price	$695	$765	$810	$910
F	Menards SKU	194-4055	194-4136	194-4217	194-4291
	Discount Price	$750	$820	$865	$965
G	Menards SKU	194-4068	194-4149	194-4220	194-4301
	Discount Price	$850	$920	$965	$1065
H	Menards SKU	194-4071	194-4152	194-4233	194-4314
	Discount Price	$945	$1015	$1060	$1160

Many of our plans are available in CAD. For availability, call or visit any **MENARDS**® store and go to the Building Materials Desk.

OTHER PRODUCTS & BUILDING AIDS

MIRROR REVERSE*
Menards SKU   194-4327
Discount Price $15

ADDITIONAL SETS**
Menards SKU   194-4330
Discount Price $45

MATERIAL LIST**
Menards SKU   100-3422
Discount Price $125

EXPRESS DELIVERY
Menards SKU   194-4356
Discount Price $40

LEGAL KIT
Menards SKU   100-3422
Discount Price $35

DETAIL PLAN PACKAGES
ELECTRICAL, PLUMBING & FRAMING - ALL SAME SKU
Menards SKU   100-3422
Discount Price $20 EA.
                 3 FOR $40

* See page 6
** Available only within 90 days after puchase of plan package of same plan

If at any time you feel you may need assistance in the field while building, HDA offers a technical assistance line for answering building questions pertaining to your specific plan. Please call 314-770-2228 Monday-Friday between 8:00am and 5:00pm CST and our professional design staff will be happy to help.

Please note: All blueprints are printed in response to your order, so we cannot honor requests for refunds. However, if for some reason you find that the plan you have purchased does not meet your requirements, you may exchange that plan for another plan in our collection within 90 days of purchase. At the time of the exchange, you will be charged a processing fee of 25% of your original plan package price, plus the difference in price between the plan packages (if applicable) and the cost to ship the new plans to you. Keep in mind, reproducible drawings can only be exchanged if the package is un-opened and material lists can only be purchased within 90 days of purchasing the plan package.

We understand that it is difficult to find blueprints for a home that will meet all your needs. That is why HDA, Inc. (Home Design Alternatives) is pleased to offer home plan modification services.

Typical home plan modifications include:

- Changing foundation type
- Adding square footage to a plan
- Changing exterior wall framing from 2x4 to 2x6
- Changing wall heights
- Changing the entry into a garage
- Changing a two-car garage to a three-car garage or making a garage larger
- Redesigning kitchen, baths, and bedrooms
- Changing exterior elevations
- Or most other home plan modifications you may desire!

Some home plan modifications we cannot make include:

- Mirror-reversing the plans
- Adapting/engineering plans to meet local building codes
- Combining parts of two different plans (due to copyright laws)

Our plan modification service is easy to use. Simply:

1. Decide on the modifications you want. For the most accurate quote, be as detailed as possible and refer to rooms in the same manner as the floor plan (i.e. if the floor plan refers to a "den," use "den" in your description). Including a sketch of the modified floor plan is always helpful.

2. Visit any **MENARDS**® Building Materials Desk and request an HDA Custom Change Form.

3. Within two business days, you or your Menards store will receive your quote - that's up to you. Quotes do not include the cost of the reproducible masters required for our designer to legally make changes. For example, if your quote is $850 and the reproducible masters for your plan are $800, your order total will be $1650 including shipping and handling charges.

4. Call the number on the quote to accept and purchase the reproducible masters from the **MENARDS**® Building Materials Desk.

5. Our designer will send you up to three drafts to verify your initial changes. Extra costs apply after the third draft. If additional changes are made that alter the original request, extra charges may be incurred.

6. Once you approve a draft with the final changes, we then make the changes to the reproducible masters by adding additional sheets. The original reproducible masters (with no changes) plus your new changed sheets will be shipped to you.

Other Important Information:

- Plans cannot be redrawn in reverse format. All modifications will be made to match the reproducible master's original layout. Once you receive the plans, you can make reverse copies at your local copy shop.

- Our staff designer will provide the first draft for your review within 4 weeks (plus shipping time) of receiving your order.

- You will receive up to three drafts to review before your original changes are modified. The first draft will totally encompass all modifications based on your original request. Additional changes not included in your original request will be charged separately at an hourly rate of $75 or a flat quoted rate.

- Modifications will be drawn on a separate sheet with the changes shown and a note to see the main sheet for details. For example, a floor plan sheet from the original set (i.e. Sheet 3) would be followed by a new floor plan sheet with changes (i.e. Sheet A-3).

- Plans are drawn to meet national building codes. Modifications will not be drawn to any particular state or county codes, thus we cannot guarantee that the revisions will meet your local building codes. You may be required to have a local architect or designer review the plans in order to have them comply with your state or county building codes.

- Time and cost estimates are good for 90 calendar days.

- All modification requests need to be submitted in writing. Verbal requests will not be accepted.

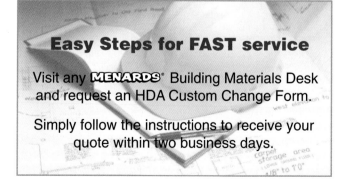

Easy Steps for FAST service

Visit any **MENARDS**® Building Materials Desk and request an HDA Custom Change Form.

Simply follow the instructions to receive your quote within two business days.

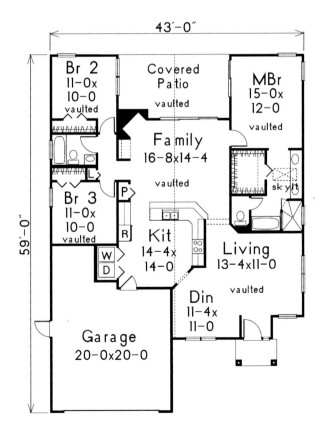

Sunridge

Vaulted Ceilings Add Dimension

1,550 total square feet of living area

Special features

- Alcove in the family room can be used as a cozy corner fireplace or as a media center
- Master bedroom features a large walk-in closet, skylight and separate tub and shower
- Convenient laundry closet
- Kitchen with pantry and breakfast bar connects to the family room
- Family room and master bedroom access the covered patio
- 3 bedrooms, 2 baths, 2-car garage
- Slab foundation

Price Code B

Delta Queen I

Layout Creates Large Open Living Area

1,285 total square feet of living area

Special features

- Accommodating home with ranch-style porch
- Large storage area on back of home
- Master bedroom includes dressing area, private bath and built-in bookcase
- Kitchen features pantry, breakfast bar and complete view to the dining room
- 3 bedrooms, 2 baths
- Crawl space foundation, drawings also include basement and slab foundations

Price Code B

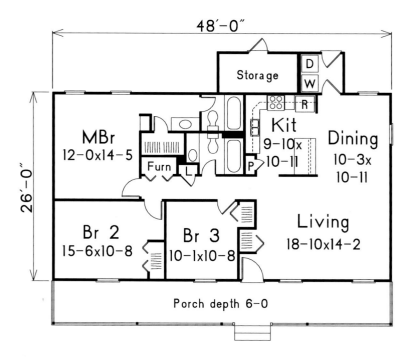

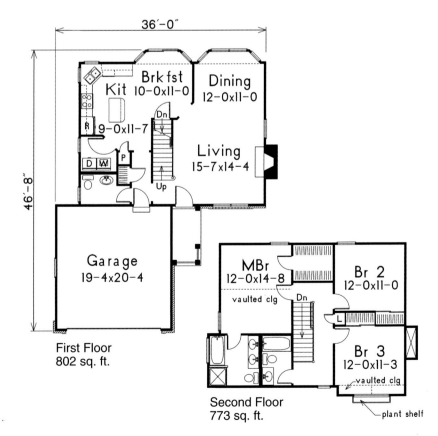

First Floor
802 sq. ft.

Second Floor
773 sq. ft.

Ashley Park

Stylish Living
For A Narrow Lot

1,575 total square feet of living area

Special features
- Inviting porch leads to spacious living and dining rooms
- Kitchen with corner windows features an island snack bar, attractive breakfast room bay, convenient laundry area and built-in pantry
- A luxury bath and walk-in closet adorn the master bedroom suite
- 3 bedrooms, 2 1/2 baths, 2-car garage
- Basement foundation, drawings also include crawl space and slab foundations

Price Code B

Summerset

Country Home With Front Orientation

2,029 total square feet of living area

Special Features

- Stonework, gables, and double porches create a country flavor
- Kitchen enjoys extravagant cabinetry and counterspace in a bay, island snack bar, built-in pantry and cheery dining area
- Angled stair descends from large entry with wood columns and is open to a vaulted great room with corner fireplace
- 4 bedrooms, 2 baths, 2-car side entry garage
- Basement foundation, drawings also include crawl space and slab foundations

Price Code D

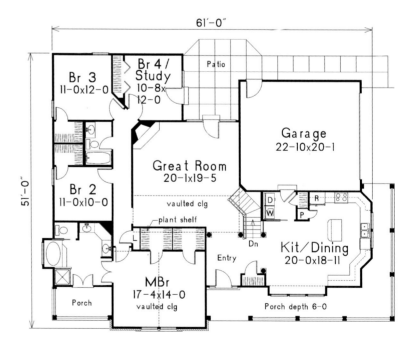

61'-0"

51'-0"

Br 3
11-0x12-0

Br 4 /
Study
10-8x
12-0

Patio

Br 2
11-0x10-0

Great Room
20-1x19-5

vaulted clg

plant shelf

Garage
22-10x20-1

Kit/Dining
20-0x18-11

MBr
17-4x14-0
vaulted clg

Entry

Dn

Porch

Porch depth 6-0

12

To order this plan, visit the Menards Building Materials Desk.

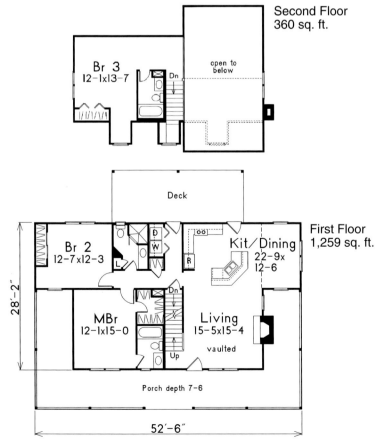

Second Floor
360 sq. ft.

Br 3
12-1x13-7

open to
below

Dn

First Floor
1,259 sq. ft.

Deck

Br 2
12-7x12-3

Kit/Dining
22-9x
12-6

D

W

R

28'-2"

MBr
12-1x15-0

Dn

Living
15-5x15-4

vaulted

Up

Porch depth 7-6

52'-6"

Hickory

Country-Style Porch Adds Charm

1,619 total square feet of living area

Special features
- Private second floor bedroom and bath
- Kitchen features a snack bar and adjacent dining area
- Master bedroom has a private bath
- Centrally located washer and dryer
- 3 bedrooms, 3 baths
- Basement foundation, drawings also include crawl space and slab foundations

Price Code B

Ryland

Classic Ranch Has Grand Appeal With Expansive Porch

1,400 total square feet of living area

Special features

- Master bedroom is secluded for privacy
- Large utility room has additional cabinet space
- Covered porch provides an outdoor seating area
- Living room and master bedroom feature vaulted ceilings
- Oversized two-car garage has storage space
- 3 bedrooms, 2 baths, 2-car garage
- Basement foundation, drawings also include crawl space foundation

Price Code B

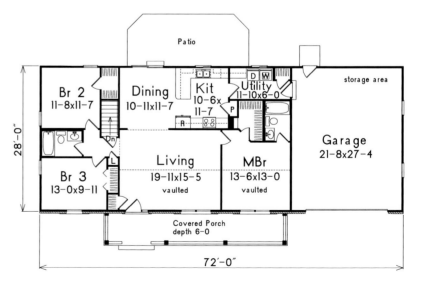

Patio

Br 2
11-8x11-7

Dining
10-11x11-7

Kit
10-6x
11-7

Utility
11-10x6-0

D W

storage area

28'-0"

Dn

P

R

Br 3
13-0x9-11

Living
19-11x15-5
vaulted

MBr
13-6x13-0
vaulted

Garage
21-8x27-4

L

Covered Porch
depth 6-0

72'-0"

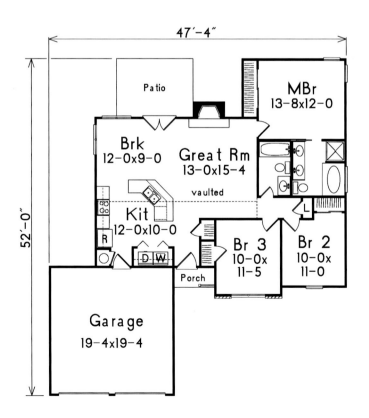

Strickland

Brick And Siding Enhance This Traditional Home

1,170 total square feet of living area

Special features
- Master bedroom enjoys privacy at the rear of this home
- Kitchen has an angled bar that overlooks the great room and breakfast area
- Living areas combine to create a greater sense of spaciousness
- Great room has a cozy fireplace
- 3 bedrooms, 2 baths, 2-car garage
- Slab foundation

Price Code AA

Brightmoore

Functional Layout For Comfortable Living

1,360 total square feet of living area

Special features

- Kitchen/dining room features an island workspace
- Master bedroom has a large walk-in closet and private bath
- Laundry room is adjacent to the kitchen for easy access
- Convenient workshop in garage
- Large closets in secondary bedrooms maintain organization
- 3 bedrooms, 2 baths, 2-car side entry garage
- Basement foundation, drawings also include crawl space and slab foundations

Price Code A

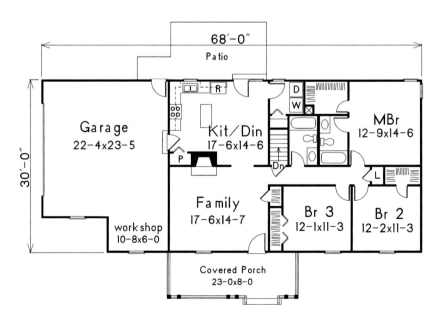

To order this plan, visit the Menards Building Materials Desk.

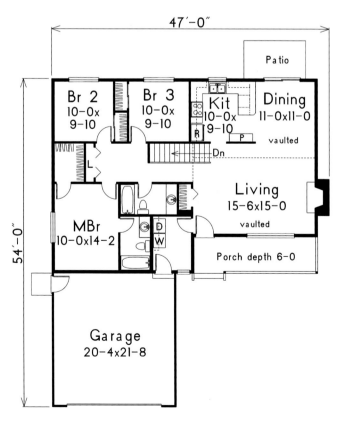

47'-0"

54'-0"

Br 2	Br 3	Kit	Dining
10-0x 9-10	10-0x 9-10	10-0x 9-10	11-0x11-0

Patio

vaulted

Dn

Living
15-6x15-0

vaulted

MBr
10-0x14-2

Porch depth 6-0

Garage
20-4x21-8

Oregon

Economical Ranch For Easy Living

1,314 total square feet of living area

Special features
- Energy efficient home with 2" x 6" exterior walls
- Covered porch adds immediate appeal and welcoming charm
- Open floor plan combined with a vaulted ceiling offers spacious living
- Functional kitchen is complete with a pantry and eating bar
- Cozy fireplace in the living room
- Private master bedroom features a large walk-in closet and bath
- 3 bedrooms, 2 baths, 2-car garage
- Basement foundation

Price Code A

To order this plan, visit the Menards Building Materials Desk.

17

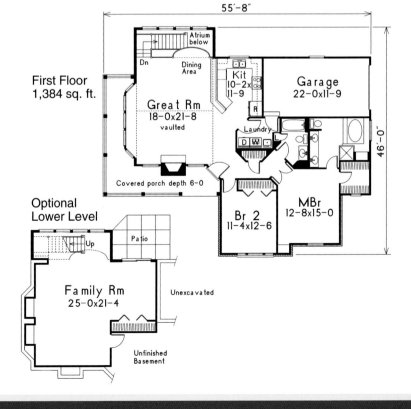

Rear View

Summerview

Tranquility Of An Atrium Cottage

1,384 total square feet of living area

Special features

- Wrap-around country porch for peaceful evenings
- Vaulted great room enjoys a large bay window, stone fireplace, pass-through kitchen and awesome rear views through an atrium window wall
- Master bedroom features a double-door entry, walk-in closet and a fabulous bath
- Atrium opens to 611 square feet of optional living area below
- 2 bedrooms, 2 baths, 1-car side entry garage
- Walk-out basement foundation

Price Code B

First Floor
1,384 sq. ft.

55'-8"

Atrium below

Dn

Dining Area

Kit 10-2x 11-9

Garage 22-0x11-9

Great Rm 18-0x21-8 vaulted

Laundry

D W

R

Covered porch depth 6-0

46'-0"

MBr 12-8x15-0

Br 2 11-4x12-6

Optional Lower Level

Up

Patio

Family Rm 25-0x21-4

Unexcavated

Unfinished Basement

18

To order this plan, visit the Menards Building Materials Desk.

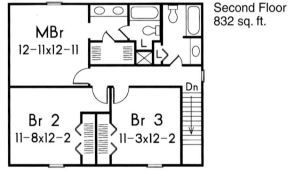

Second Floor
832 sq. ft.

MBr
12-11x12-11

Br 2
11-8x12-2

Br 3
11-3x12-2

Dn

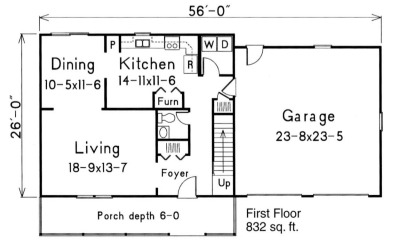

56'-0"

26'-0"

Dining
10-5x11-6

Kitchen
14-11x11-6

P · R · W D

Furn

Living
18-9x13-7

Foyer

Up

Garage
23-8x23-5

Porch depth 6-0

First Floor
832 sq. ft.

Country Charm I

Old-Fashioned Porch Adds Welcoming Appeal

1,664 total square feet of living area

Special features

- L-shaped country kitchen includes pantry and cozy breakfast area
- Bedrooms are located on the second floor for privacy
- Master bedroom includes a walk-in closet, dressing area and bath
- 2" x 6" exterior walls available, please order plan #M02-001D-0121
- 3 bedrooms, 2 1/2 baths, 2-car garage
- Crawl space foundation, drawings also include basement and slab foundations

Price Code B

To order this plan, visit the Menards Building Materials Desk.

19

Sabrina

Pillared Front Porch Generates Charm And Warmth

1,567 total square feet of living area

Special features

- Energy efficient home with 2" x 6" exterior walls
- Living room flows into the dining room shaped by an angled pass-through into the kitchen
- Cheerful, windowed dining area
- Future area available on the second floor has an additional 338 square feet of living area
- 3 bedrooms, 2 baths, 2-car side entry garage
- Partial basement/crawl space foundation, drawings also include slab foundation

Price Code C

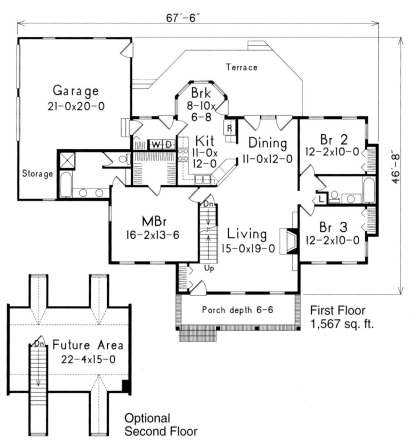

67'-6"

46'-8"

Garage
21-0x20-0

Terrace

Brk
8-10x
6-8

Storage

Kit
11-0x
12-0

W D

Dining
11-0x12-0

Br 2
12-2x10-0

MBr
16-2x13-6

Dn

Living
15-0x19-0

Up

Br 3
12-2x10-0

Porch depth 6-6

First Floor
1,567 sq. ft.

Future Area
22-4x15-0

Dn

Optional
Second Floor

Spring Hill

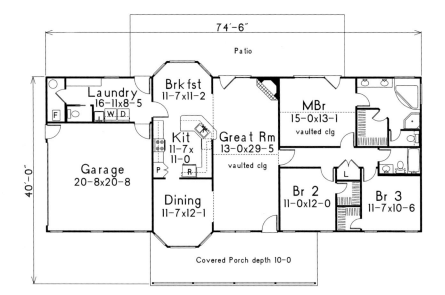

Bedrooms Separate From Rest Of Home

1,849 total square feet of living area

Special features

- Enormous laundry/mud room has many extras including a storage area and half bath
- Secondary bedrooms include walk-in closets
- Kitchen has a wrap-around eating counter and is positioned between the formal dining area and breakfast room for convenience
- 3 bedrooms, 2 1/2 baths, 2-car side entry garage
- Slab foundation, drawings also include crawl space foundation

Price Code C

Woodfield

Dining With A View

1,524 total square feet of living area

Special features

- Delightful balcony overlooks two-story entry illuminated by an oval window
- Roomy first floor master bedroom offers quiet privacy
- All bedrooms feature one or more walk-in closets
- 3 bedrooms, 2 1/2 baths, 2-car garage
- Basement foundation, drawings also include crawl space and slab foundations

Price Code B

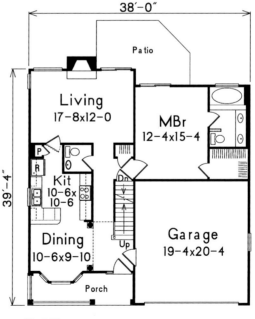

First Floor
951 sq. ft.

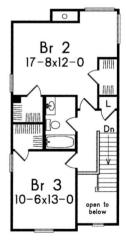

Second Floor
573 sq. ft.

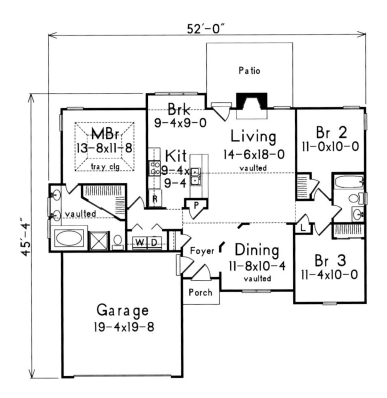

Morris

Stonework Entry Adds Character To This Home

1,358 total square feet of living area

Special features
- Vaulted master bath has a walk-in closet, double-bowl vanity, large tub, shower and toilet area
- Galley kitchen opens to both the living room and the breakfast area
- A vaulted ceiling joins the dining and living rooms
- Breakfast room has a full wall of windows
- 3 bedrooms, 2 baths, 2-car garage
- Slab foundation

Price Code A

To order this plan, visit the Menards Building Materials Desk.

23

Glenmore

Vaulted Ceilings Enhance Spacious Home

2,073 total square feet of living area

Special features

- Family room provides an ideal gathering area with a fireplace, large windows and vaulted ceiling
- Private first floor master bedroom enjoys a vaulted ceiling and luxury bath
- Kitchen features an angled bar connecting it to the breakfast area
- 4 bedrooms, 2 1/2 baths, 2-car side entry garage
- Basement foundation

Price Code D

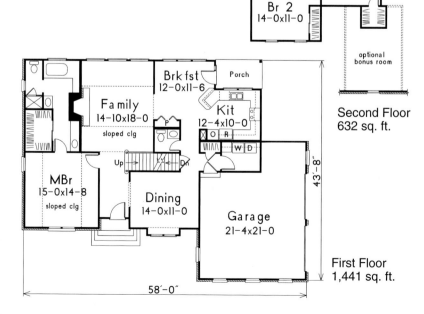

Br 3
12-0x10-0

Br 4
12-0x10-0

Br 2
14-0x11-0

optional bonus room

Second Floor
632 sq. ft.

Brk fst
12-0x11-6

Porch

Family
14-10x18-0
sloped clg

Kit
12-4x10-0

MBr
15-0x14-8
sloped clg

Up

Dn

Dining
14-0x11-0

Garage
21-4x21-0

43-8"

58'-0"

First Floor
1,441 sq. ft.

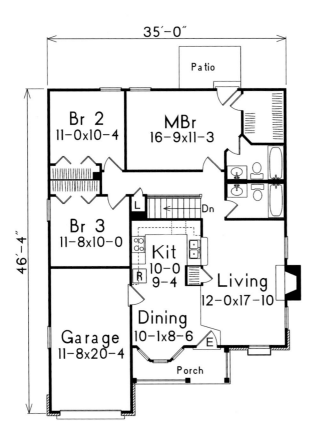

Glen Ellen

Country Charm For A Small Lot

1,169 total square feet of living area

Special features
- Front facade features a distinctive country appeal
- Living room enjoys a wood-burning fireplace and pass-through to kitchen
- A stylish U-shaped kitchen offers an abundance of cabinet and counterspace with a view to the living room
- The master bedroom features a large walk-in closet, access to the rear patio and a private bath
- 3 bedrooms, 2 baths, 1-car garage
- Basement foundation

Price Code AA

Brookfield

Country Style With Wrap-Around Porch

1,597 total square feet of living area

Special features

- Spacious family room includes a fireplace and coat closet
- Open kitchen and dining room provide a breakfast bar and access to the outdoors
- Convenient laundry area is located near the kitchen
- Secluded master bedroom enjoys a walk-in closet and private bath
- 4 bedrooms, 2 1/2 baths, 2-car detached garage
- Basement foundation

Price Code C

Second Floor
615 sq. ft.

Br 3
14-0x10-0

Br 4
12-0x12-4

Br 2
14-0x10-10

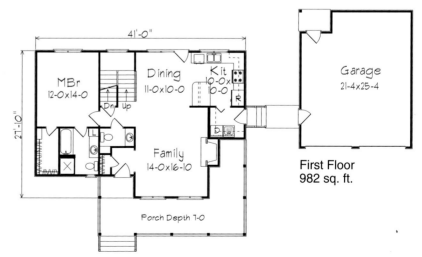

First Floor
982 sq. ft.

41'-0"

21'-10"

MBr
12-0x14-0

Dining
11-0x10-0

Kit
10-0x 10-0

Family
14-0x16-10

Garage
21-4x25-4

Porch Depth 7-0

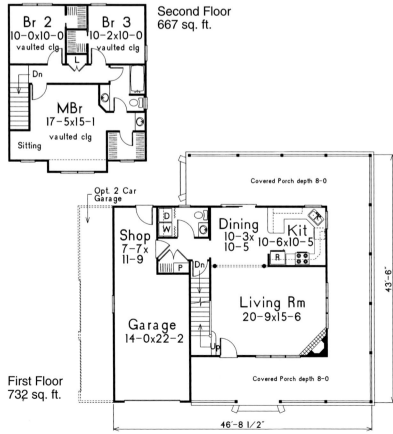

Second Floor
667 sq. ft.

Br 2
10-0x10-0
vaulted clg

Br 3
10-2x10-0
vaulted clg

L

Dn

MBr
17-5x15-1
vaulted clg

Sitting

Opt. 2 Car Garage

Shop
7-7x
11-9

Dining
10-3x
10-5

Kit
10-6x10-5

Garage
14-0x22-2

Dn

P

Up

Living Rm
20-9x15-6

Covered Porch depth 8-0

Covered Porch depth 8-0

43'-6"

46'-8 1/2"

First Floor
732 sq. ft.

Caroline

Covered Porch Surrounds Home

1,399 total square feet of living area

Special features

- Living room overlooks the dining area through arched columns
- Laundry room contains a handy half bath
- Spacious master bedroom includes a sitting area, walk-in closet and plenty of sunlight
- 3 bedrooms, 1 1/2 baths, 1-car garage
- Basement foundation, drawings also include crawl space and slab foundations

Price Code A

Westham

Organized Kitchen Is The Center Of Activity

1,882 total square feet of living area

Special features

- Handsome brick facade
- Spacious great room and dining area combination is brightened by unique corner windows and patio access
- Well-designed kitchen incorporates a breakfast bar peninsula, sweeping casement window above sink and a walk-in pantry island
- 4 bedrooms, 2 baths, 2-car side entry garage
- Basement foundation

Price Code C

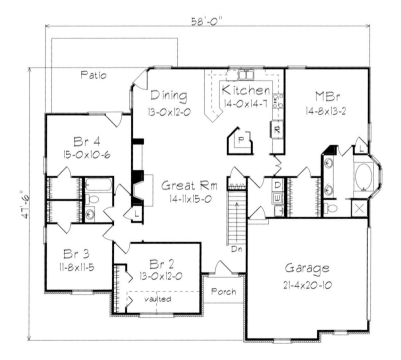

To order this plan, visit the Menards Building Materials Desk.

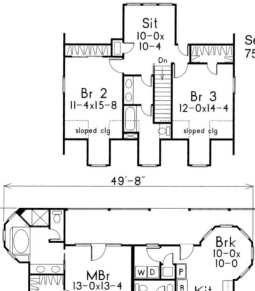

Second Floor
751 sq. ft.

First Floor
1,308 sq. ft.

49'-8"

38'-4"

Sit
10-0x
10-4

Dn

Br 2
11-4x15-8

Br 3
12-0x14-4

sloped clg   sloped clg

Brk
10-0x
10-0

W D   P

R

MBr
13-0x13-4

Kit
12-0x
10-0

Living
17-4x17-0

Up

Dining
12-4x14-0

Veranda depth 7-0

Springwood

Country Charm Wrapped In A Veranda

2,059 total square feet of living area

Special features

- Octagon-shaped breakfast room offers plenty of windows and creates a view to the veranda
- First floor master bedroom has a large walk-in closet and deluxe bath
- 9' ceilings throughout the home
- 3 bedrooms, 2 1/2 baths, 2-car detached garage
- Slab foundation, drawings also include basement and crawl space foundations

Price Code C

Foxport

Three Bedroom Luxury In A Small Home

1,161 total square feet of living area

Special features

- Brickwork and feature window add elegance to this home for a narrow lot
- Living room enjoys a vaulted ceiling, fireplace and opens to the kitchen
- U-shaped kitchen offers a breakfast area with bay window, snack bar and built-in pantry
- 3 bedrooms, 2 baths
- Basement foundation

Price Code AA

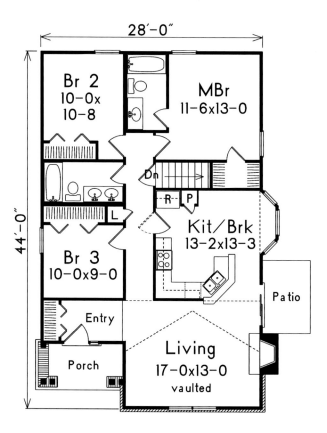

28'-0"

44'-0"

Br 2
10-0x
10-8

MBr
11-6x13-0

Dn

R   P

Kit/Brk
13-2x13-3

Br 3
10-0x9-0

L

Patio

Entry

Porch

Living
17-0x13-0
vaulted

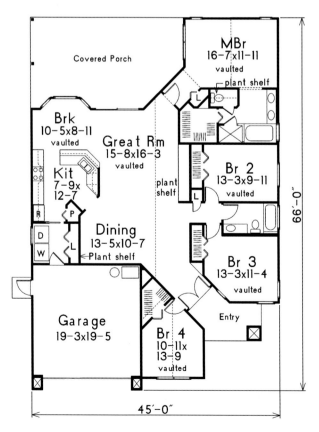

Wyndham

Wonderful Great Room

1,865 total square feet of living area

Special features

- The large foyer opens into an expansive dining area and great room
- Home features vaulted ceilings throughout
- Master bedroom features an angled entry, vaulted ceiling, plant shelf and bath with double vanity, tub and shower
- 4 bedrooms, 2 baths, 2-car garage
- Slab foundation, drawings also include crawl space foundation

Price Code D

To order this plan, visit the Menards Building Materials Desk.

31

Fairmont

Four Bedroom Home For A Narrow Lot

1,452 total square feet of living area

Special features

- Large living room features a cozy corner fireplace, bayed dining area and access from the entry with guest closet
- Forward master bedroom enjoys having its own bath and linen closet
- Three additional bedrooms share a bath with a double-bowl vanity
- 4 bedrooms, 2 baths
- Basement foundation

Price Code A

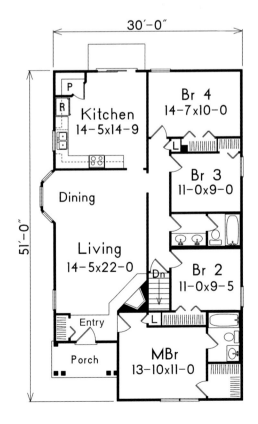

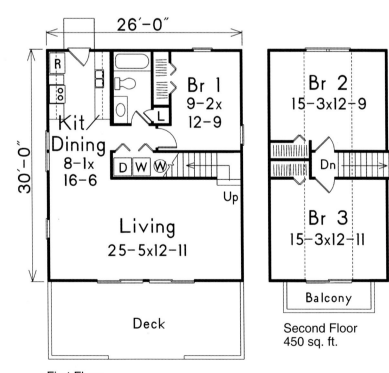

26'-0"

30'-0"

R

Kit
Dining
8-1x
16-6

Br 1
9-2x
12-9

L

D W W

Up

Living
25-5x12-11

Deck

First Floor
780 sq. ft.

Br 2
15-3x12-9

Dn

Br 3
15-3x12-11

Balcony

Second Floor
450 sq. ft.

Lakewood

Perfect Vacation Home

1,230 total square feet of living area

Special features

- Spacious living room accesses huge deck
- Bedroom #3 features a balcony overlooking the deck
- Kitchen with dining area accesses the outdoors
- Washer and dryer are tucked under the stairs for space efficiency
- 3 bedrooms, 1 bath
- Crawl space foundation, drawings also include slab foundation

Price Code A

Sycamore

Open Ranch Design Gives Expansive Look

1,630 total square feet of living area

Special features

- Crisp facade and full windows front and back offer open viewing
- Wrap-around rear deck is accessible from the breakfast room, dining room and master bedroom
- Vaulted ceilings top the living room and master bedroom
- Sitting area and large walk-in closet complement the master bedroom
- 3 bedrooms, 2 baths, 2-car garage
- Basement foundation

Price Code B

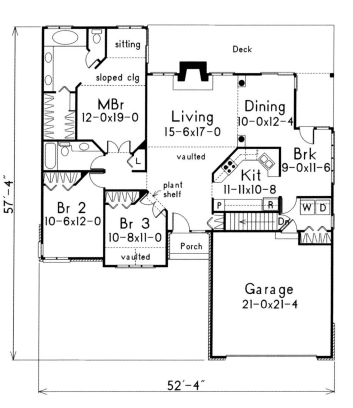

Second Floor
988 sq. ft.

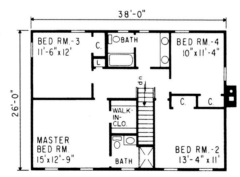

38'-0"

26'-0"

BED RM.-3
11'-6"x12'

BATH

BED RM.-4
10"x11'-4"

C.

WALK-
IN-
CLO.

MASTER
BED RM.
15'x12'-9"

BED RM.-2
13'-4" x 11'

BATH

C.   C.

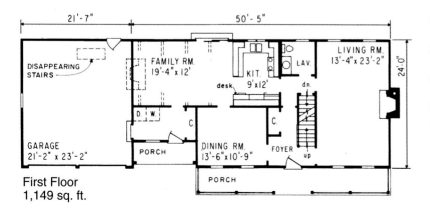

21'-7"   50'-5"

24'-0"

DISAPPEARING
STAIRS

FAMILY RM.
19'-4" x 12'

LAV.

LIVING RM.
13'-4" x 23'-2"

KIT.
9'x12'

desk

dn.

D.   W.

C.

C.

GARAGE
21'-2" x 23'-2"

PORCH

DINING RM.
13'-6"x10'-9"

FOYER

up

PORCH

First Floor
1,149 sq. ft.

Countrystone

Country Styling With Splendid Floor Plan

2,137 total square feet of living area

Special features

- Spacious porch for plants, chairs and family gatherings
- Huge living room includes front and rear views
- U-shaped kitchen features abundant storage
- Laundry room with large closet has its own porch
- 4 bedrooms, 2 1/2 baths, 2-car garage
- Partial basement/crawl space foundation

Price Code C

Norwick

Great Room's Symmetry Steals The Show

1,985 total square feet of living area

Special features

- Charming design for a narrow lot
- Dramatic sunken great room features a vaulted ceiling, large double-hung windows and transomed patio doors
- Grand master bedroom includes a double-door entry, large closet, elegant bath and patio access
- 4 bedrooms, 3 1/2 baths, 2-car garage
- Basement foundation

Price Code C

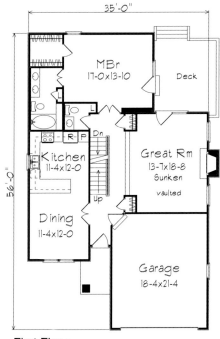

35'-0"

56'-0"

MBr
17-0x13-10

Deck

Kitchen
11-4x12-0

Dn

R - P

Up

Great Rm
13-7x18-8
Sunken

vaulted

Dining
11-4x12-0

Garage
18-4x21-4

First Floor
1,114 sq. ft.

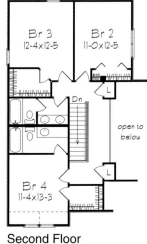

Br 3
12-4x12-5

Br 2
11-0x12-5

Dn

open to below

L

Br 4
11-4x13-3

Second Floor
871 sq. ft.

To order this plan, visit the Menards Building Materials Desk.

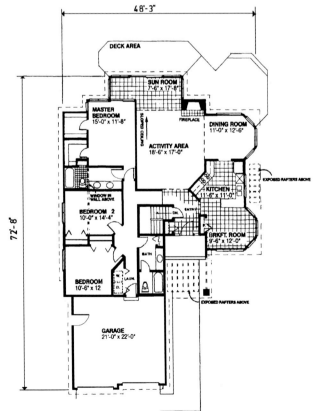

Montebello

Smartly Elegant

1,907 total square feet of living area

Special features
- Activity area with fireplace opens to the dining room
- Sun room off activity area leads to the deck
- Laundry room is conveniently located in the bedroom wing of the home
- Two bedrooms share a full bath
- Master bedroom suite features access to the sun room plus a deluxe master bath with clerestory window
- 3 bedrooms, 2 baths, 2-car garage
- Partial basement/crawl space foundation

Price Code C

To order this plan, visit the Menards Building Materials Desk.

37

Barclay

Striking, Covered Arched Entry

1,859 total square feet of living area

Special features
- Fireplace highlights the vaulted great room
- Master bedroom includes a large closet and private bath
- Kitchen adjoins breakfast room providing easy access to the outdoors
- 3 bedrooms, 2 1/2 baths, 2-car garage
- Basement foundation

Price Code D

Second Floor
789 sq. ft.

Br 2
10-8x11-3

MBr
11-10x17-2

Dn

open to below

Br 3
11-8x10-2

First Floor
1,070 sq. ft.

63'-4"

36'-0"

Brk
9-8x 11-6

Kit
10-0x13-8

Great Rm
15-2x19-0

P

Dn

vaulted

Up

Foyer

Dining
11-8x11-2

Garage
21-8x21-8

38

To order this plan, visit the Menards Building Materials Desk.

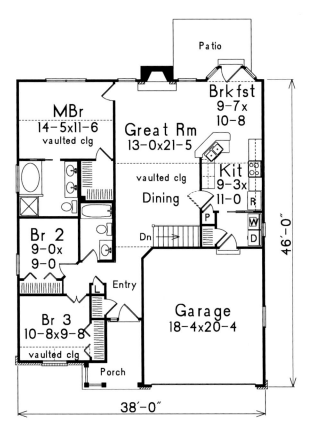

Ashmont

Distinguished Styling For A Small Lot

1,268 total square feet of living area

Special features

- Multiple gables, large porch and arched windows create a classy exterior
- Innovative design provides openness in the great room, kitchen and breakfast room
- Secondary bedrooms have private hall with bath
- 3 bedrooms, 2 baths, 2-car garage
- Basement foundation, drawings also include crawl space and slab foundations

Price Code B

To order this plan, visit the Menards Building Materials Desk.

39

Springdale

Stylish Retreat For A Narrow Lot

1,084 total square feet of living area

Special features

- Delightful country porch for quiet evenings
- The living room offers a front feature window which invites the sun and includes a fireplace and dining area with private patio
- The U-shaped kitchen features lots of cabinets and a bayed breakfast room with built-in pantry
- Both bedrooms have walk-in closets and access to their own bath
- 2 bedrooms, 2 baths
- Basement foundation

Price Code AA

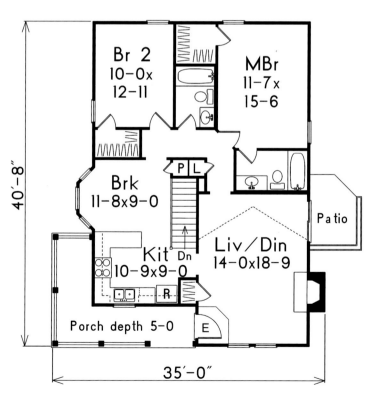

Br 2
10-0x
12-11

MBr
11-7x
15-6

P L

Brk
11-8x9-0

Patio

Kit
10-9x9-0
Dn

Liv/Din
14-0x18-9

R

E

Porch depth 5-0

40'-8"

35'-0"

Sparrow

Compact Ranch With Good Looks

1,120 total square feet of living area

Special features

- Energy efficient home with 2" x 6" exterior walls
- Porch and shuttered windows with lower accent panels add greatly to this home's appeal
- Kitchen offers a snack counter and opens to the family room
- Carport includes building for ample storage
- 3 bedrooms, 1 1/2 baths, 1-car carport
- Basement foundation, drawings also include crawl space and slab foundations

Price Code A

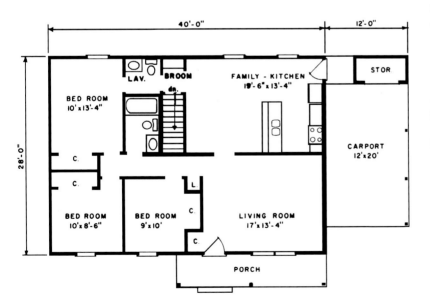

Rosedale

Stately Covered Front Entry

2,089 total square feet of living area

Special features

- Family room features a fireplace, built-in bookshelves and triple sliders opening to the covered patio
- Kitchen overlooks the family room and features a pantry and desk
- Master bedroom becomes a quiet retreat with patio access
- Master bedroom features an oversized bath with walk-in closet and corner tub
- 4 bedrooms, 3 baths, 2-car garage
- Slab foundation

Price Code C

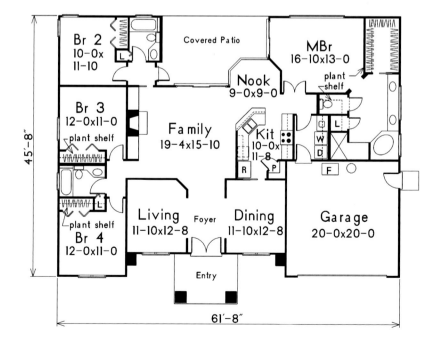

Br 2
10-0x
11-10

Covered Patio

MBr
16-10x13-0

plant shelf

Nook
9-0x9-0

Br 3
12-0x11-0

plant shelf

Family
19-4x15-10

Kit
10-0x
11-8

W
D

L

R   P

F

45'-8"

plant shelf

Living
11-10x12-8

Foyer

Dining
11-10x12-8

Garage
20-0x20-0

plant shelf

Br 4
12-0x11-0

Entry

61'-8"

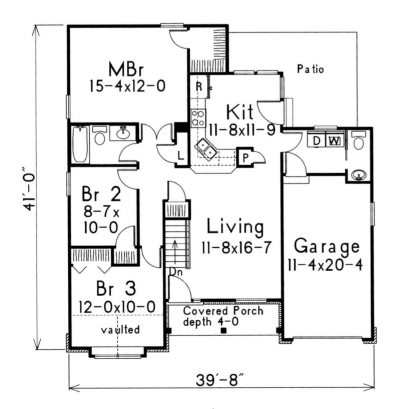

Hathaway

Innovative Ranch Has Cozy Corner Patio

1,092 total square feet of living area

Special features

- A box window and inviting porch with dormers create a charming facade
- Eat-in kitchen offers a pass-through breakfast bar, corner window wall to patio, pantry and convenient laundry with half bath
- Master bedroom features a double-door entry and walk-in closet
- 3 bedrooms, 1 1/2 baths, 1-car garage
- Basement foundation

Price Code AA

To order this plan, visit the Menards Building Materials Desk.

43

Springfield

Charming Home Arranged For Open Living

1,609 total square feet of living area

Special features

- Kitchen captures full use of space with pantry, ample cabinets and workspace
- Master bedroom is well secluded with a walk-in closet and private bath
- Large utility room includes a sink and extra storage
- Attractive bay window in the dining area provides light
- 3 bedrooms, 2 1/2 baths, 2-car garage
- Slab foundation

Price Code B

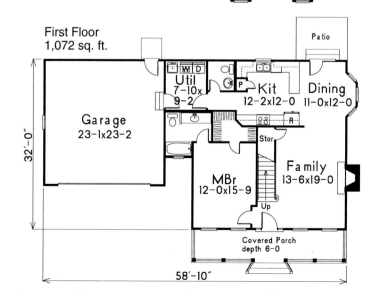

Second Floor
537 sq. ft.

attic

Br 2
12-0x11-10
sloped clg.

Br 3
11-0x11-10
sloped clg.

Dn

First Floor
1,072 sq. ft.

Patio

Util
7-10x
9-2

Kit
12-2x12-0

Dining
11-0x12-0

Garage
23-1x23-2

32'-0"

Stor

MBr
12-0x15-9

Family
13-6x19-0

Up

Covered Porch
depth 6-0

58'-10"

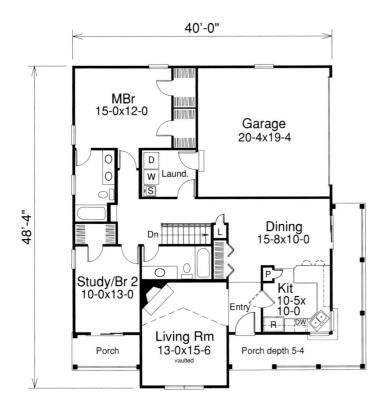

40'-0"

MBr
15-0x12-0

Garage
20-4x19-4

D
W Laund.
S

48'-4"

Dn

Dining
15-8x10-0

Study/Br 2
10-0x13-0

Entry

P

Kit
10-5x
10-0

R   DW

Living Rm
13-0x15-6
vaulted

Porch

Porch depth 5-4

Springhill

Porches Enhance Small Retirement Or Starter Home

1,316 total square feet of living area

Special features
- Porches are accessible from entry, dining room and bedroom #2
- The living room enjoys a vaulted ceiling, corner fireplace and twin windows with an arched transom
- A kitchen is provided with corner windows, an outdoor plant shelf, a snack bar, a built-in pantry and opens to a large dining room
- 2 bedrooms, 2 baths, 2-car side entry garage
- Basement foundation, drawings also include crawl space and slab foundations

Price Code A

Bonham

Spacious Living In This Ranch

1,433 total square feet of living area

Special features

- Vaulted living room includes a cozy fireplace and an oversized entertainment center
- Bedrooms #2 and #3 share a full bath
- Master bedroom has a full bath and large walk-in closet
- 3 bedrooms, 2 baths, 2-car garage
- Basement foundation, drawings also include crawl space and slab foundations

Price Code A

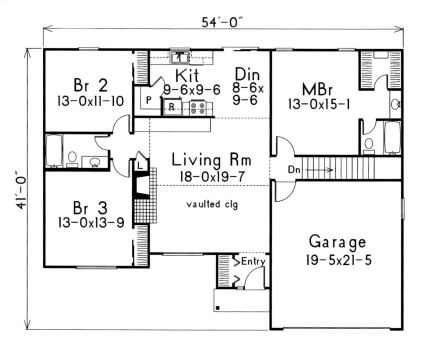

54'-0"

41'-0"

Br 2
13-0x11-10

Kit
9-6x9-6

Din
8-6x
9-6

MBr
13-0x15-1

P

R

Living Rm
18-0x19-7

vaulted clg

Dn

Br 3
13-0x13-9

L

Entry

Garage
19-5x21-5

46

To order this plan, visit the Menards Building Materials Desk.

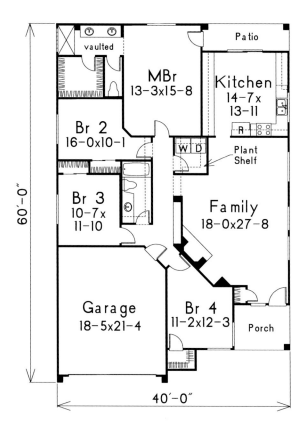

Haywood

Inviting Covered Corner Entry

1,747 total square feet of living area

Special features
- Entry opens into large family room with coat closet, angled fireplace and attractive plant shelf
- Kitchen and master bedroom access covered patio
- Functional kitchen includes ample workspace
- 4 bedrooms, 2 baths, 2-car garage
- Slab foundation

Price Code B

La Valencia

Great Room And Kitchen Symmetry Dominates Design

1,712 total square feet of living area

Special features

- Stylish stucco exterior enhances curb appeal
- Sunken great room offers corner fireplace flanked by 9' wide patio doors
- Well-designed kitchen features ideal view of the great room and fireplace through breakfast bar opening
- 3 bedrooms, 2 1/2 baths, 2-car garage
- Crawl space foundation

Price Code B

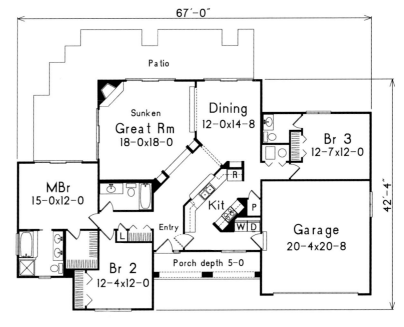

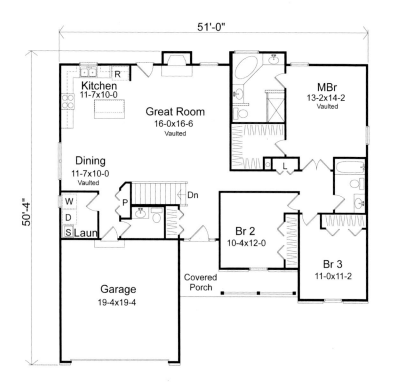

Foristell

Stunning Family Home

1,635 total square feet of living area

Special features
- The covered porch creates an inviting facade
- A whirlpool tub and twin vanities add elegance to the master bedroom bath
- The kitchen island provides extra workspace and also offers an easy way to serve buffet dinners
- 3 bedrooms, 2 1/2 baths, 2-car garage
- Basement foundation

Price Code AA

Corsica

Roomy Two-Story Has Covered Porch

1,600 total square feet of living area

Special features

- Energy efficient home with 2" x 6" exterior walls
- First floor master bedroom is accessible from two points of entry
- Master bath dressing area includes separate vanities and a mirrored makeup counter
- Second floor bedrooms have generous storage space and share a full bath
- 3 bedrooms, 2 baths, 2-car side entry garage
- Crawl space foundation, drawings also include slab foundation

Price Code B

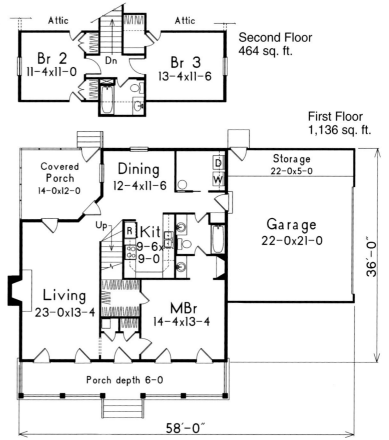

Attic

Attic

Br 2
11-4x11-0

Dn

Br 3
13-4x11-6

Second Floor
464 sq. ft.

First Floor
1,136 sq. ft.

Covered Porch
14-0x12-0

Dining
12-4x11-6

D
W

Storage
22-0x5-0

Up

R Kit
9-6x 9-0

Garage
22-0x21-0

36'-0"

Living
23-0x13-4

MBr
14-4x13-4

Porch depth 6-0

58'-0"

50

To order this plan, visit the Menards Building Materials Desk.

Penbrooke

Vaulted Great Room

1,895 total square feet of living area

Special features

- The foyer opens into the airy great room that features a grand fireplace
- The kitchen/breakfast area enjoys a work island, built-in desk, walk-in pantry and access to the outdoors
- Both baths include a double vanity for convenience
- 2" x 6" exterior walls available, please order plan #M02-058D-0094
- 3 bedrooms, 2 baths, 2-car garage
- Basement foundation

Price Code B

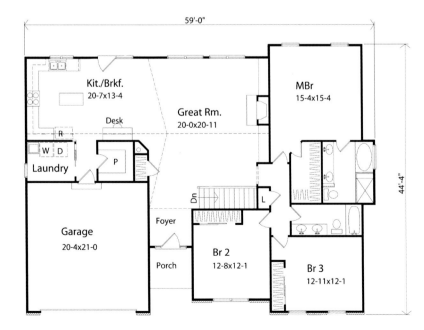

To order this plan, visit the Menards Building Materials Desk.

51

MENARDS®

Parkdale

Two-Story Country Home Features Large Living Areas

1,998 total square feet of living area

Special features
- Family room features a fireplace and access to the kitchen and dining area
- Skylights add daylight to the second floor baths
- Utility room is conveniently located near the garage and kitchen
- Kitchen/breakfast area includes a pantry, island workspace and easy access to the patio
- 3 bedrooms, 2 1/2 baths, 2-car side entry garage
- Basement foundation, drawings also include crawl space and slab foundations

Price Code D

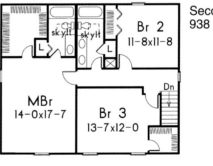

Second Floor
938 sq. ft.

Br 2
11-8x11-8

MBr
14-0x17-7

Br 3
13-7x12-0

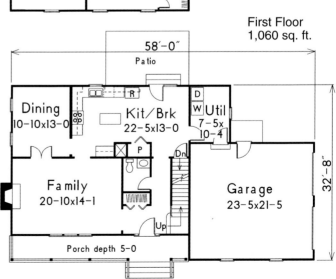

First Floor
1,060 sq. ft.

58'-0"

Patio

Dining
10-10x13-0

Kit/Brk
22-5x13-0

Util
7-5x 10-4

Family
20-10x14-1

Garage
23-5x21-5

32'-8"

Porch depth 5-0

26'-0"

44'-0"

FAMILY ROOM
13'-0" x 11'-6"

P.R.

DN.

BACK PORCH

REF.

DINING ROOM
13'-0" x 10'-0"

KITCHEN
8'-3" x 10'-0"

PANTRY

DN.

UP

ACTIVITY AREA
13'-0" x 17'-1"

VERANDA

DN.

BEDROOM 2
10'-8" x 10'-0"

BATH

L

L

DN.

MASTER BEDROOM
13'-0" x 14'-7"

BALCONY

First Floor
1,092 sq. ft.

Second Floor
570 sq. ft.

Appleton

Victorian Detailing Adds Interest

1,662 total square feet of living area

Special features

- Activity area becomes an ideal place for family gatherings
- Well-organized kitchen includes lots of storage space, a walk-in pantry and plenty of cabinetry
- The rear of the home features a versatile back porch for dining or relaxing
- Master bedroom has a bay window and private balcony
- 2 bedrooms, 1 1/2 baths
- Basement foundation

Price Code B

Grandview

Spacious A-Frame

1,769 total square feet of living area

Special features

- Living room boasts an elegant cathedral ceiling and fireplace
- U-shaped kitchen and dining area combine for easy living
- Secondary bedrooms include double closets
- Secluded master bedroom features a sloped ceiling, large walk-in closet and private bath
- 2" x 6" exterior walls available, please order plan #M02-001D-0124
- 3 bedrooms, 2 baths
- Basement foundation, drawings also include crawl space and slab foundations

Price Code B

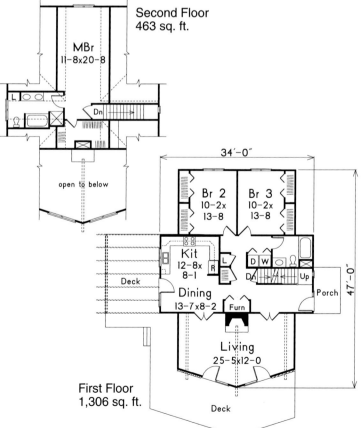

Second Floor
463 sq. ft.

MBr
11-8x20-8

Dn

open to below

34'-0"

Br 2
10-2x
13-8

Br 3
10-2x
13-8

Kit
12-8x
8-1

Deck

Dining
13-7x8-2

Furn

Porch

Up

47'-0"

Living
25-5x12-0

First Floor
1,306 sq. ft.

Deck

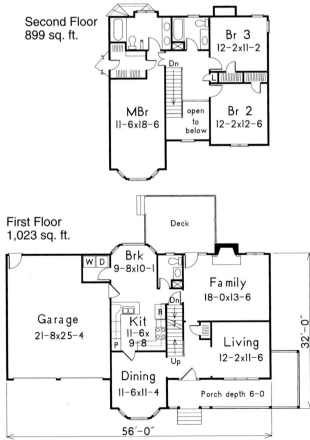

Second Floor
899 sq. ft.

Br 3
12-2x11-2

Dn

MBr
11-6x18-6

open
to
below

Br 2
12-2x12-6

First Floor
1,023 sq. ft.

Deck

Brk
9-8x10-1

W D

Family
18-0x13-6

Dn

Garage
21-8x25-4

Kit
11-6x
9-8

R

Living
12-2x11-6

P

Up

32'-0"

Dining
11-6x11-4

Porch depth 6-0

56'-0"

Ridgeview

Two-Story Foyer Adds To Country Charm

1,922 total square feet of living area

Special features

- Varied front elevation features numerous accents
- Master bedroom suite is well-secluded with double-door entry and private bath
- Formal living and dining rooms located off the entry
- 3 bedrooms, 2 1/2 baths, 2-car garage
- Basement foundation

Price Code C

MENARDS®

Donnelly

Designed For Handicap Access

1,578 total square feet of living area

Special features
■ Plenty of closet, linen and storage space
■ Covered porches in the front and rear of home add charm to this design
■ Open floor plan has a unique angled layout
■ 3 bedrooms, 2 baths, 2-car garage
■ Basement foundation

Price Code B

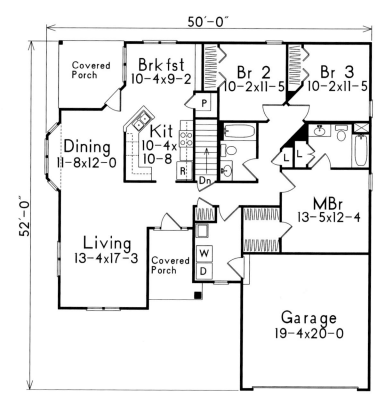

50'-0"

52'-0"

Covered Porch

Brk fst
10-4x9-2

Br 2
10-2x11-5

Br 3
10-2x11-5

Dining
11-8x12-0

Kit
10-4x
10-8

P

R

Dn

L L

MBr
13-5x12-4

Living
13-4x17-3

Covered Porch

W
D

Garage
19-4x20-0

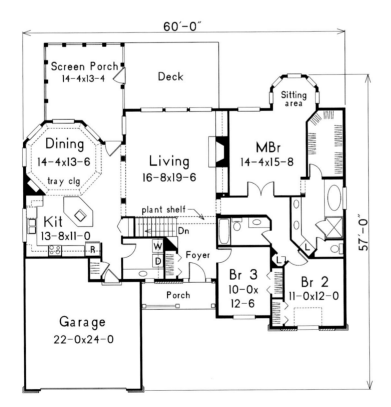

Dennison

Open Living Centers On Windowed Dining Room

2,003 total square feet of living area

Special features

- Energy efficient home with 2" x 6" exterior walls
- Octagon-shaped dining room boasts a tray ceiling and deck overlook
- L-shaped island kitchen serves the living and dining rooms
- Master bedroom boasts a luxury bath and walk-in closet
- Living room features columns, elegant fireplace and a 10' ceiling
- 3 bedrooms, 2 baths, 2-car garage
- Basement foundation

Price Code D

To order this plan, visit the Menards Building Materials Desk.

57

MENARDS®

Lexburg

Open Layout Ensures Easy Living

976 total square feet of living area

Special features

- Cozy front porch opens into the large living room
- Convenient half bath is located on the first floor
- All bedrooms are located on the second floor for privacy
- Dining room has access to the outdoors
- 3 bedrooms, 1 1/2 baths
- Basement foundation

Price Code AA

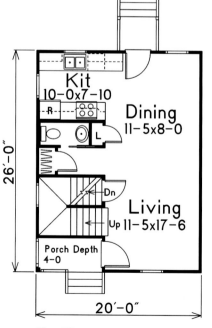

Kit
10-0x7-10

Dining
11-5x8-0

Living
Up 11-5x17-6

Dn

Porch Depth
4-0

26'-0"

20'-0"

First Floor
488 sq. ft.

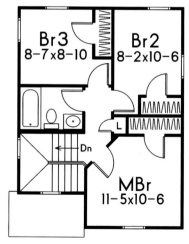

Br3
8-7x8-10

Br2
8-2x10-6

L

Dn

MBr
11-5x10-6

Second Floor
488 sq. ft.

Twinbrooke

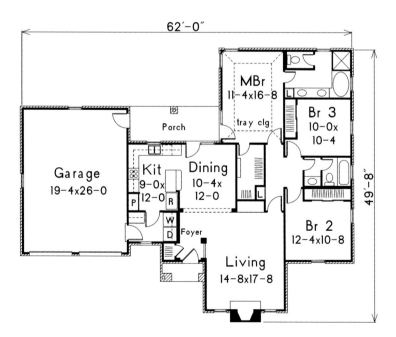

Built-In Media Center Is Focal Point In Living Room

1,539 total square feet of living area

Special features

- Standard 9' ceilings
- Master bedroom features 10' tray ceiling, access to porch, ample closet space and full bath
- Serving counter separates kitchen and dining room
- Foyer with handy coat closet opens to living area with fireplace
- Handy utility room near kitchen
- 3 bedrooms, 2 baths, 2-car garage
- Slab foundation

Price Code B

To order this plan, visit the Menards Building Materials Desk.

59

Wellington

Practical Two-Story, Full Of Features

2,058 total square feet of living area

Special features

- Handsome two-story foyer with balcony creates a spacious entrance area
- Vaulted master bedroom has a private dressing area and large walk-in closet
- Skylights furnish natural lighting in the hall and master bath
- 3 bedrooms, 2 1/2 baths, 2-car garage
- Basement foundation, drawings also include slab and crawl space foundations

Price Code C

Br 3
11-0x13-5

skylt

skylt

W D

L

L

MBr
16-5x13-5
vaulted

Dn

Br 2
13-0x11-0

open to below

Second Floor
960 sq. ft.

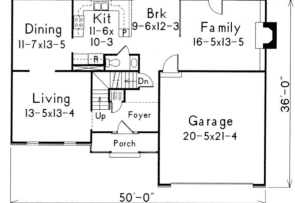

First Floor
1,098 sq. ft.

Deck

Dining
11-7x13-5

Kit
11-6x
10-3

P

Brk
9-6x12-3

Family
16-5x13-5

R

Dn

Living
13-5x13-4

Up

Foyer

Garage
20-5x21-4

Porch

36'-0"

50'-0"

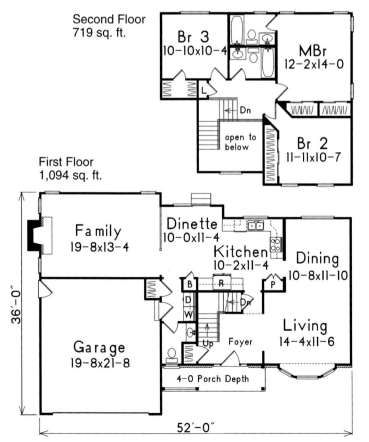

Second Floor
719 sq. ft.

Br 3
10-10x10-4

MBr
12-2x14-0

Dn

open to below

Br 2
11-11x10-7

First Floor
1,094 sq. ft.

Family
19-8x13-4

Dinette
10-0x11-4

Kitchen
10-2x11-4

Dining
10-8x11-10

B R P

D
W

Dn

Living
14-4x11-6

Up Foyer

Garage
19-8x21-8

36'-0"

4-0 Porch Depth

52'-0"

Mapleview

Great Plan For Formal And Informal Entertaining

1,813 total square feet of living area

Special features

- Bedrooms are located on the second floor for privacy
- Living room with large bay window joins the dining room for expansive formal entertaining
- The family room, dinette and kitchen combine for an impressive living area
- Two-story foyer and L-shaped stairs create a dramatic entry
- Inviting covered porch
- 3 bedrooms, 2 1/2 baths, 2-car garage
- Basement foundation

Price Code D

Mercer

Efficient Kitchen Layout

1,598 total square feet of living area

Special features

- Additional storage area in garage
- Double-door entry into master bedroom with luxurious master bath
- Entry opens into large family room with vaulted ceiling and open stairway to basement
- 3 bedrooms, 2 baths, 2-car garage
- Basement foundation

Price Code B

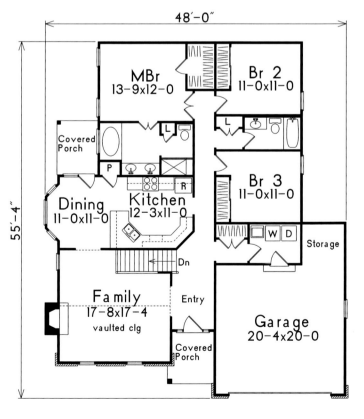

Second Floor
532 sq. ft.

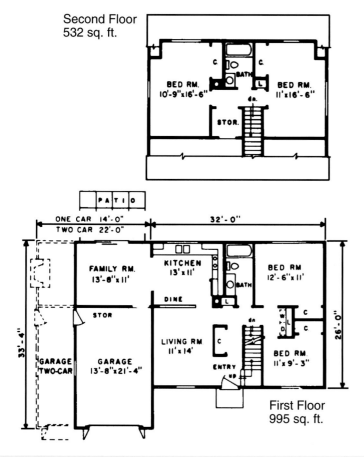

First Floor
995 sq. ft.

Leesville

Home With Focus On Family

1,527 total square feet of living area

Special features

- Impressive wood staircase graces the entrance foyer
- L-shaped kitchen with dine-in area opens to the family room with patio views
- Two bedrooms and an oversized hall bath share a private hall
- Two large bedrooms, a convenient hall bath and large storage closet comprise the second floor
- 4 bedrooms, 2 baths, 1-car garage
- Basement or crawl space foundation, please specify when ordering

Price Code B

Florence

Comfortable One-Story Country Home

1,367 total square feet of living area

Special features

- Energy efficient home with 2" x 6" exterior walls
- Neat front porch shelters the entrance
- Dining room has a full wall of windows and storage area
- Breakfast area leads to the rear terrace through sliding doors
- The large living room features a high ceiling, skylight and fireplace
- 3 bedrooms, 2 baths, 2-car garage
- Basement foundation, drawings also include slab foundation

Price Code B

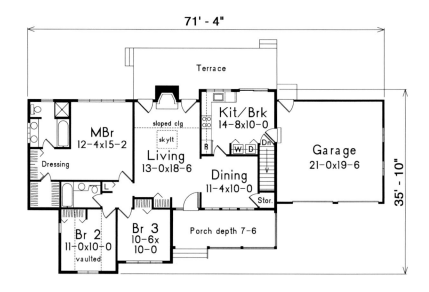

64

To order this plan, visit the Menards Building Materials Desk.

Woodford

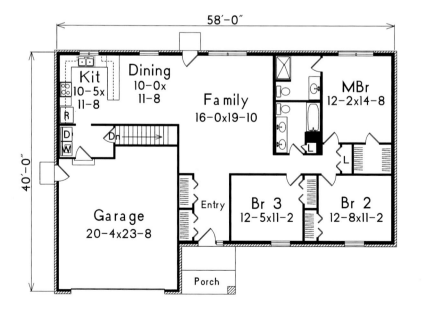

Distinctive One-Level Living

1,605 total square feet of living area

Special features

- Detailed entry is highlighted with a stone floor and double guest closets
- The well-designed kitchen includes an open view to the family room
- The third bedroom can be easily utilized as a den with optional bi-fold doors off the entry
- 3 bedrooms, 2 baths, 2-car garage
- Basement foundation, drawings also include crawl space and slab foundations

Price Code B

Ferguson

Well-Sculptured Design, Inside And Out

1,759 total square feet of living area

Special features

- The striking entry is created by a unique stair layout, an open high ceiling and a fireplace
- Bonus area over garage, which is included in the square footage, could easily convert to a fourth bedroom or activity center
- Second floor bedrooms share a private dressing area and bath
- 3 bedrooms, 2 1/2 baths, 2-car garage
- Basement foundation

Price Code B

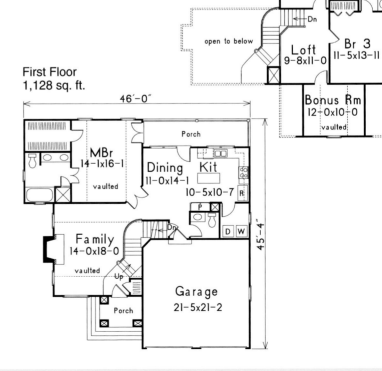

Second Floor
631 sq. ft.

Br 2
13–3x14–1

Loft
9–8x11–0

Br 3
11–5x13–11

Bonus Rm
12–0x10–0
vaulted

First Floor
1,128 sq. ft.

46'–0"

45'–4"

MBr
14–1x16–1
vaulted

Porch

Dining
11–0x14–1

Kit
10–5x10–7

Family
14–0x18–0
vaulted

Garage
21–5x21–2

Porch

66

To order this plan, visit the Menards Building Materials Desk.

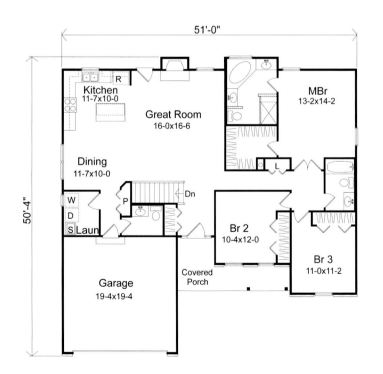

Arborway

Dormer Adds Curb Appeal

1,635 total square feet of living area

Special features

- The open atmosphere of the combined kitchen, dining and great rooms makes this a perfect space to gather with family and friends
- When it's time to relax, retreat to the luxurious master bedroom equipped with a deluxe bath
- A half bath, laundry room and pantry at the garage entrance add function to this family friendly home
- 3 bedrooms, 2 1/2 baths, 2-car garage
- Basement foundation

Price Code AA

Lexington

Dramatic Layout Created By Victorian Turret

2,050 total square feet of living area

Special features

- Large kitchen and dining area have access to garage and porch
- Master bedroom features a unique turret design, private bath and large walk-in closet
- Laundry facilities are conveniently located near the bedrooms
- 2" x 6" exterior walls available, please order plan #M02-001D-0112
- 3 bedrooms, 2 1/2 baths, 2-car side entry garage
- Basement foundation, drawings also include crawl space and slab foundations

Price Code C

Second Floor
1,022 sq. ft.

Br 2
13-9x10-5

Br 3
9-4x
13-5

skylts

W D

skylt

MBr
11-8x19-0

Dn

40'-0"

57'-4"

Garage
23-5x23-8

Kit
11-5x13-5

Din
10-0x13-5

Family
17-5x13-5

Porch

raised ceiling

Furn.

Living
11-8x19-0

Foyer

Up

Dn

Porch

First Floor
1,028 sq. ft.

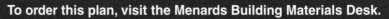

Second Floor
784 sq. ft.

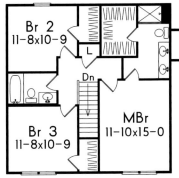

Br 2
11-8x10-9

L

Dn

MBr
11-10x15-0

Br 3
11-8x10-9

48'-0"

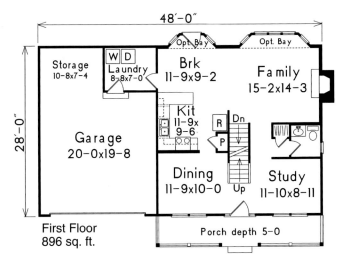

Opt. Bay   Opt. Bay

Storage
10-8x7-4

W D
Laundry
8-8x7-0

Brk
11-9x9-2

Family
15-2x14-3

28'-0"

Kit
11-9x
9-6

R

Dn

P

Garage
20-0x19-8

Dining
11-9x10-0

Up

Study
11-10x8-11

First Floor
896 sq. ft.

Porch depth 5-0

Smithsonian

Open Floor Plan With Extra Amenities

1,680 total square feet of living area

Special features
- Compact and efficient layout in an affordable package
- Second floor has three bedrooms all with oversized closets
- All bedrooms are located on the second floor for privacy
- 3 bedrooms, 2 1/2 baths, 2-car garage
- Basement foundation

Price Code B

Chesterton

Distinctive Two-Level Living

1,980 total square feet of living area

Special features

- Curb appeal is captured with multi-level roof, gables and palladian windows
- Step down into a magnificent living and activity room adorned with cozy fireplace, wet bar, pass-through to kitchen and lots of glass area
- A delightful sitting room accesses the second floor bedrooms and offers a view to the step-up foyer below
- 3 bedrooms, 2 1/2 baths, 2-car garage
- Basement foundation

Price Code C

Second Floor
643 sq. ft.

BEDROOM
11'-9" x 13'-2"

SITTING ROOM
8'-6" x 17'-5"

OPEN BELOW TO FOYER

DN.

L.

BEDROOM
14'-2" x 10'-5"

BATH

ATTIC STORAGE SPACE

50'-8"

KITCHEN
13'-0" x 14'-0"
D.W.

MASTER BEDROOM
15'-0" x 13'-8"

ACTIVITY AREA
21'-4" x 12'-0"

REF.

WET BAR

DN.

LIVING ROOM
13'-0" x 11'-6"

D.

W.

LAUN.

P.R.

BATH

UP

47'-0"

UP

GARAGE
22'-0" x 21'-6"

UP

First Floor
1,337 sq. ft.

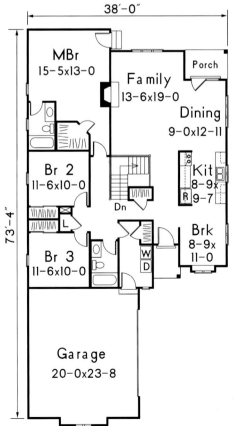

Floor plan dimensions: 38'-0" × 73'-4"

- MBr 15-5x13-0
- Family 13-6x19-0
- Porch
- Dining 9-0x12-11
- Br 2 11-6x10-0
- Dn
- Kit 8-9x 9-7
- Br 3 11-6x10-0
- Brk 8-9x 11-0
- W D
- L
- R
- Garage 20-0x23-8

Baxter

Ideal Ranch For A Narrow Lot

1,624 total square feet of living area

Special features
- Master bedroom has a private entry from the outdoors
- Garage is adjacent to the utility room with convenient storage closet
- Large family and dining areas feature a fireplace and porch access
- Pass-through kitchen opens directly to the cozy breakfast area
- 3 bedrooms, 2 baths, 2-car side entry garage
- Basement foundation, drawings also include crawl space and slab foundations

Price Code B

To order this plan, visit the Menards Building Materials Desk.

71

MENARDS®

Sherbrooke

Circle-Top Windows Adorn The Foyer

1,516 total square feet of living area

Special features

- On the second floor the stairway looks out over the living room
- Master bedroom enjoys first floor privacy and a luxurious bath
- Kitchen has easy access to the deck, laundry closet and garage
- 3 bedrooms, 2 1/2 baths, 2-car garage
- Basement foundation

Price Code B

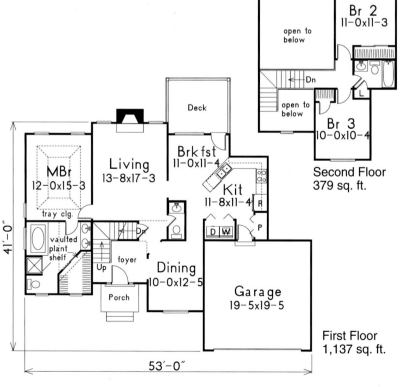

Br 2
11-0x11-3

open to below

Dn

open to below

Br 3
10-0x10-4

Second Floor
379 sq. ft.

Deck

Brk fst
11-0x11-4

Living
13-8x17-3

MBr
12-0x15-3

tray clg.

vaulted plant shelf

Kit
11-8x11-4

Up

foyer

Dining
10-0x12-5

Porch

Garage
19-5x19-5

41'-0"

53'-0"

First Floor
1,137 sq. ft.

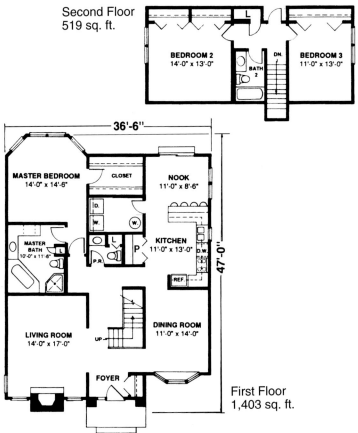

Second Floor
519 sq. ft.

BEDROOM 2
14'-0" x 13'-0"

BATH
2

DN.

BEDROOM 3
11'-0" x 13'-0"

36'-6"

MASTER BEDROOM
14'-0" x 14'-6"

CLOSET

NOOK
11'-0" x 8'-6"

D.

W.

W.

KITCHEN
11'-0" x 13'-0"

MASTER
BATH
10'-0" x 11'-6"

P

D.W.

P.R.

REF

47'-0"

LIVING ROOM
14'-0" x 17'-0"

UP

DINING ROOM
11'-0" x 14'-0"

FOYER

First Floor
1,403 sq. ft.

Winslow

Terrific Cottage-Style Design

1,922 total square feet of living area

Special features

- Master bedroom includes many luxuries such as an oversized private bath and large walk-in closet
- The kitchen is spacious with a functional eat-in breakfast bar and is adjacent to the nook which is ideal as a breakfast room
- Plenty of storage is featured in both bedrooms on the second floor and in the hall
- Enormous utility room is centrally located on the first floor
- 3 bedrooms, 2 1/2 baths
- Basement foundation

Price Code C

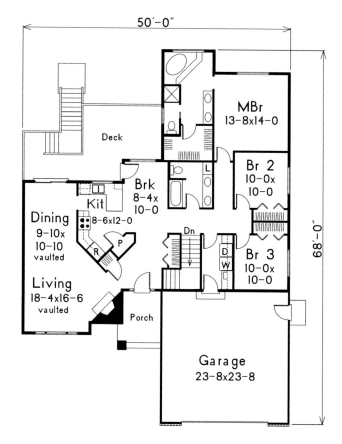

Jackson

Vaulted Living Area Adds Appeal

1,689 total square feet of living area

Special features
- Energy efficient home with 2" x 6" exterior walls
- Open living and dining area includes a vaulted ceiling, corner fireplace and access to the rear deck
- Stylish angled kitchen offers large counter workspace and nook
- Master bedroom boasts a spacious bath with step-up tub, and large walk-in closet
- 3 bedrooms, 2 baths, 2-car garage
- Basement foundation, drawings also include slab and crawl space foundations

Price Code B

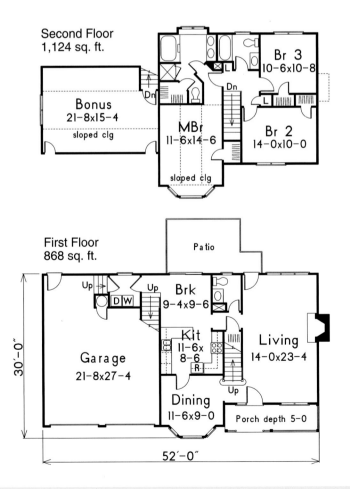

Second Floor
1,124 sq. ft.

Bonus
21-8x15-4
sloped clg

Br 3
10-6x10-8

Dn

L

Dn

MBr
11-6x14-6

Br 2
14-0x10-0

sloped clg

First Floor
868 sq. ft.

Patio

Up

Up

Brk
9-4x9-6

DW

30'-0"

Kit
11-6x
8-6

Living
14-0x23-4

Garage
21-8x27-4

R

Up

Dining
11-6x9-0

Porch depth 5-0

52'-0"

Hollyhill

Double Bay Enhances Front Entry

1,992 total square feet of living area

Special features

- Distinct living, dining and breakfast areas
- Master bedroom boasts a full-end bay window and a cathedral ceiling
- Storage and laundry area are located adjacent to the garage
- Bonus room over the garage for future office or playroom is included in the square footage
- 3 bedrooms, 2 1/2 baths, 2-car garage
- Crawl space foundation, drawings also include basement foundation

Price Code C

Treebrooke

Country Kitchen Is Center Of Living Activities

1,556 total square feet of living area

Special features

- A compact home with all the amenities
- Country kitchen combines practicality with access to other areas for eating and entertaining
- Two-way fireplace joins the dining and living areas
- Plant shelf and vaulted ceiling highlight the master bedroom
- 3 bedrooms, 2 1/2 baths, 2-car garage
- Basement foundation

Price Code B

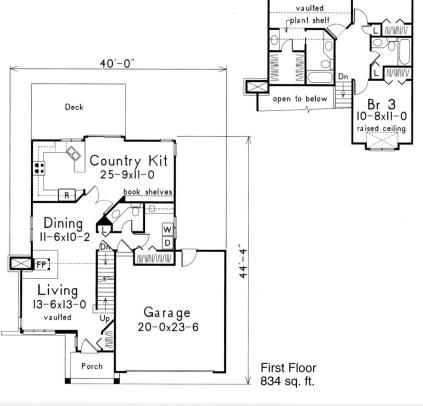

Second Floor
722 sq. ft.

MBr
14-10x12-0
vaulted
plant shelf

Br 2
10-8x11-0

open to below

Dn

Br 3
10-8x11-0
raised ceiling

40'-0"

Deck

Country Kit
25-9x11-0
book shelves

R

Dining
11-6x10-2

W
D

44'-4"

FP

Living
13-6x13-0
vaulted

Up

Dn

Garage
20-0x23-6

Porch

First Floor
834 sq. ft.

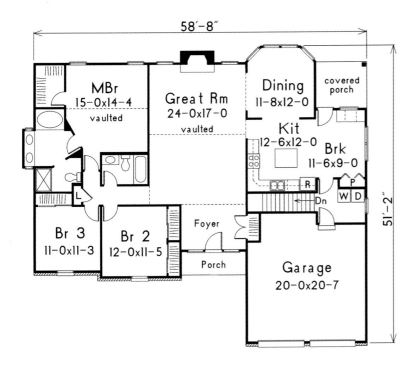

58'-8"

MBr
15-0x14-4
vaulted

Great Rm
24-0x17-0
vaulted

Dining
11-8x12-0

covered
porch

Kit
12-6x12-0

Brk
11-6x9-0

L

Br 3
11-0x11-3

Br 2
12-0x11-5

Foyer

Porch

Dn

W D

P

R

51'-2"

Garage
20-0x20-7

Mooreland

Traditional Exterior, Handsome Accents

1,882 total square feet of living area

Special features

- Wide, handsome entrance opens to the vaulted great room with fireplace
- Private covered porch extends breakfast area
- Practical passageway runs through the laundry room from the garage to the kitchen
- Vaulted ceiling in master bedroom
- 3 bedrooms, 2 baths, 2-car garage
- Basement foundation

Price Code D

Kelli

Welcoming Front Porch, A Country Touch

2,043 total square feet of living area

Special features

- Energy efficient home with 2" x 6" exterior walls
- Two-story central foyer includes two coat closets
- Large combined space is provided by the kitchen, family and breakfast rooms
- Breakfast nook for informal dining looks out to the deck and screened porch
- 3 bedrooms, 2 1/2 baths, 2-car side entry garage
- Basement foundation, drawings also include slab foundation

Price Code D

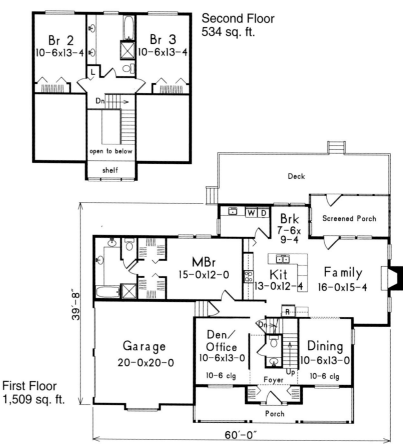

Second Floor
534 sq. ft.

Br 2
10-6x13-4

Br 3
10-6x13-4

Dn

open to below

shelf

Deck

W D

Brk
7-6x
9-4

Screened Porch

MBr
15-0x12-0

Kit
13-0x12-4

Family
16-0x15-4

39'-8"

Garage
20-0x20-0

Den/
Office
10-6x13-0

10-6 clg

Dn

R

Foyer

Up

Dining
10-6x13-0

10-6 clg

First Floor
1,509 sq. ft.

Porch

60'-0"

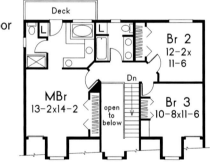

Second Floor
863 sq. ft.

Deck

Br 2
12-2x
11-6

MBr
13-2x14-2

open to below

Dn

Br 3
10-8x11-6

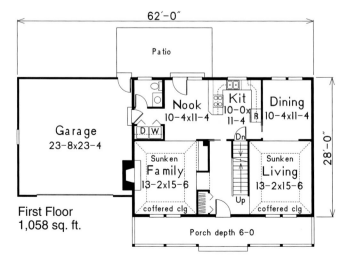

62'-0"

Patio

Garage
23-8x23-4

Nook
10-4x11-4

Kit
10-0x
11-4

Dining
10-4x11-4

Sunken
Family
13-2x15-6
coffered clg

Dn

Up

Sunken
Living
13-2x15-6
coffered clg

28'-0"

First Floor
1,058 sq. ft.

Porch depth 6-0

Clifton

Country Classic With Modern Floor Plan

1,921 total square feet of living area

Special features

- Energy efficient home with 2" x 6" exterior walls
- Sunken family room includes a built-in entertainment center and coffered ceiling
- Master bedroom dressing area has double sinks, spa tub, shower and French door to private deck
- Large front porch adds to home's appeal
- 3 bedrooms, 2 1/2 baths, 2-car garage
- Basement foundation

Price Code D

Cloverdale

Classic Colonial Design With Dormers

1,967 total square feet of living area

Special features

- Double staircases in front and back of home are ideal for convenience
- Kitchen, dining and gathering rooms combine creating a multi-purpose room
- Optional studio loft above garage provides an additional 364 square feet for an office or hobby area
- 3 bedrooms, 2 baths, 2-car garage
- Partial basement/crawl space foundation, drawings also include crawl space and slab foundations

Price Code D

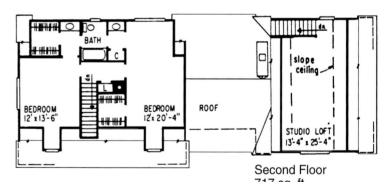

Second Floor
717 sq. ft.

First Floor
1,250 sq. ft.

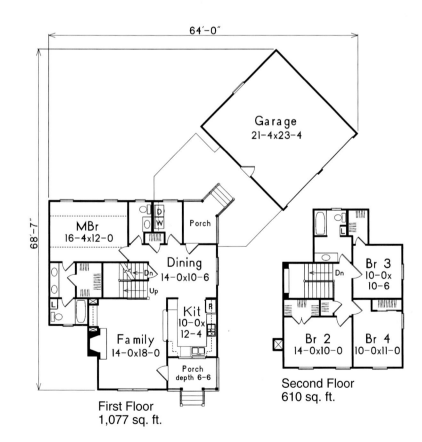

First Floor
1,077 sq. ft.

Second Floor
610 sq. ft.

Elmfield

Master Bedroom Provides Retreat

1,687 total square feet of living area

Special features
- Family room with built-in cabinet and fireplace is the focal point of this home
- U-shaped kitchen has a bar that opens to the family room
- Back porch opens to the dining room and leads to the garage via a walkway
- Convenient laundry room is located near the center of activity
- 4 bedrooms, 2 1/2 baths, 2-car detached garage
- Basement foundation

Price Code B

To order this plan, visit the Menards Building Materials Desk.

81

Highland

Trendsetting Appeal For A Narrow Lot

1,294 total square feet of living area

Special features

- Great room features a fireplace and large bay with windows and patio doors
- Enjoy a laundry room immersed in light with large windows, an arched transom and attractive planter box
- Bedroom #2 boasts a vaulted ceiling, plant shelf and half bath, perfect for a studio
- 2 bedrooms, 1 full bath, 2 half baths, 1-car rear entry garage
- Basement foundation

Price Code A

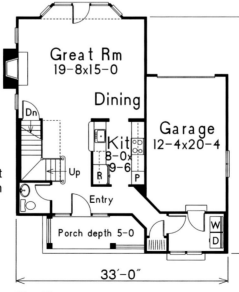

First Floor
718 sq. ft.

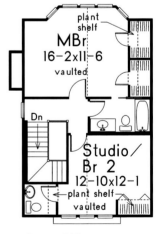

Second Floor
576 sq. ft.

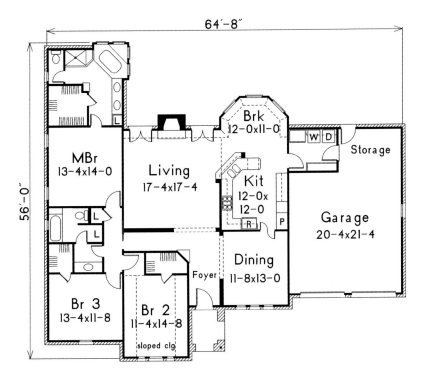

64'-8"

56'-0"

MBr
13-4x14-0

Living
17-4x17-4

Brk
12-0x11-0

W D

Storage

Kit
12-0x
12-0

R

P

Garage
20-4x21-4

Dining
11-8x13-0

Foyer

Br 3
13-4x11-8

Br 2
11-4x14-8

sloped clg

Lindenwood

Comfortable Family Living In This Ranch

1,994 total square feet of living area

Special features

- Convenient entrance from the garage into the main living area through the utility room
- Bedroom #2 features a 12' vaulted ceiling and the dining room boasts a 10' ceiling
- Entry leads to the formal dining room and attractive living room with double French doors and fireplace
- 3 bedrooms, 2 baths, 2-car garage
- Slab foundation

Price Code D

To order this plan, visit the Menards Building Materials Desk.

83

Iroquois

Well-Designed Ranch With Plenty Of Space

1,820 total square feet of living area

Special features

- Living room has a stunning cathedral ceiling
- Spacious laundry room with easy access to kitchen, garage and the outdoors
- Plenty of closet space throughout
- Covered front porch enhances outdoor living
- 3 bedrooms, 2 baths, 2-car garage
- Basement foundation

Price Code C

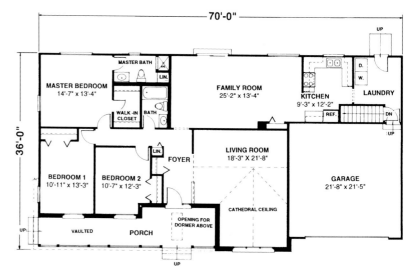

Seymour

Cheerful Ranch

1,418 total square feet of living area

Special features

- The kitchen, breakfast and great rooms combine for an easy flow of family functions
- A coat closet at the garage entrance helps to maintain organization
- All bedrooms are generous in size and the master bedroom enjoys a walk-in closet and private bath
- 3 bedrooms, 2 baths, 2-car garage
- Basement foundation

Price Code AA

Summerhill

Charming Extras Add Character To This Home

1,880 total square feet of living area

Special features

- Master bedroom is enhanced with a coffered ceiling
- Generous family and breakfast areas are modern and functional
- The front porch complements the front facade
- 3 bedrooms, 2 1/2 baths, 2-car drive under garage
- Basement foundation

Price Code C

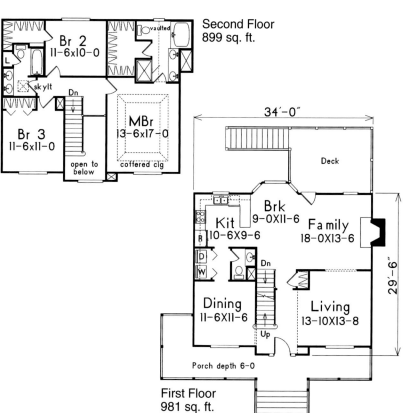

Second Floor
899 sq. ft.

Br 2
11-6x10-0

vaulted

Br 3
11-6x11-0

MBr
13-6x17-0

coffered clg

open to below

skylt

Dn

34'-0"

Deck

Brk
9-0X11-6

Kit
10-6X9-6

Family
18-0X13-6

29'-6"

Dining
11-6X11-6

Living
13-10X13-8

Dn

Up

Porch depth 6-0

First Floor
981 sq. ft.

86

To order this plan, visit the Menards Building Materials Desk.

Ashridge

Atrium Living For Views On A Narrow Lot

1,231 total square feet of living area

Special features

- Dutch gables and stone accents provide an enchanting appearance
- The spacious living room offers a masonry fireplace, and atrium with window wall
- Kitchen has a breakfast counter, lots of cabinet space and glass sliding doors to a balcony
- 380 square feet of optional living area on the lower level
- 2 bedrooms, 2 baths, 1-car drive under garage
- Walk-out basement foundation

Price Code A

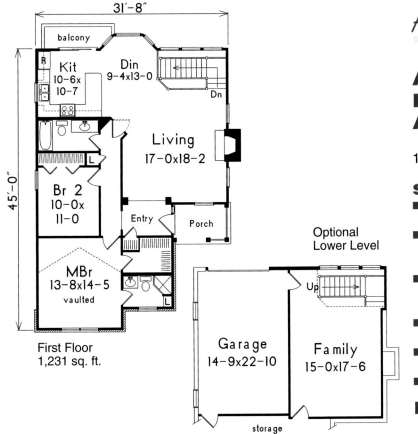

31'-8"

balcony

Kit
10-6x
10-7

Din
9-4x13-0

Dn

45'-0"

Living
17-0x18-2

Br 2
10-0x
11-0

Entry

Porch

MBr
13-8x14-5
vaulted

First Floor
1,231 sq. ft.

Optional
Lower Level

Up

Garage
14-9x22-10

Family
15-0x17-6

storage

Grantville

Private Bedrooms

1,902 total square feet of living area

Special features

- Wrap-around kitchen counter plus an island provides plenty of counterspace
- The foyer opens into the expansive vaulted great room providing an impressive entrance
- The laundry area conveniently includes a half bath and walk-in closet
- 3 bedrooms, 2 1/2 baths, 3-car garage
- Basement foundation

Price Code C

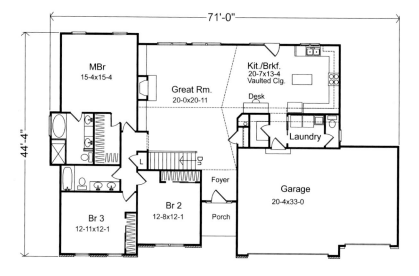

88

To order this plan, visit the Menards Building Materials Desk.

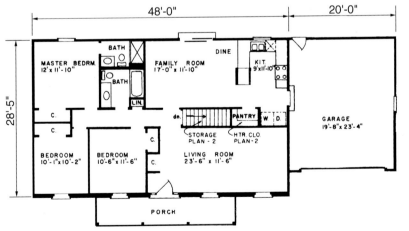

Parktown

Multi-Roof Levels Create Attractive Colonial Home

1,364 total square feet of living area

Special features

- Well-planned U-shaped kitchen features a laundry closet, built-in pantry and open peninsula
- Master bedroom has its own bath with 4' shower
- Convenient to the kitchen is an oversized two-car garage with service door to rear
- 3 bedrooms, 2 baths, 2-car garage
- Basement foundation, drawings also include crawl space and slab foundations

Price Code A

Allendale

Stone Entry Accents This Stately Two-Story

1,776 total square feet of living area

Special features

- Master bedroom has a double-door entry into the formal living room
- Large foyer has plenty of room for greeting guests
- Great room is open to the second floor and features a fireplace flanked by windows
- 3 bedrooms, 2 1/2 baths, 2-car side entry garage
- Walk-out basement foundation

Price Code B

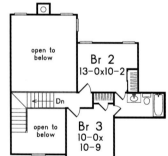

Second Floor
380 sq. ft.

open to below

Br 2
13-0x10-2

Dn

open to below

Br 3
10-0x
10-9

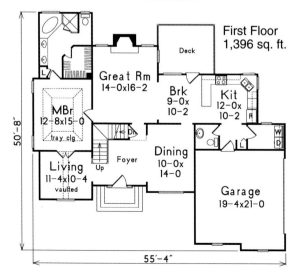

First Floor
1,396 sq. ft.

Deck

Great Rm
14-0x16-2

Brk
9-0x
10-2

Kit
12-0x
10-2

MBr
12-8x15-0
tray clg

Living
11-4x10-4
vaulted

Up

Foyer

Dining
10-0x
14-0

Garage
19-4x21-0

50'-8"

55'-4"

Wellesly

Timeless Country Facade

1,977 total square feet of living area

Special features

- An enormous entry with adjacent dining area and powder room leads to a splendid two-story family room with fireplace
- Kitchen features an abundance of cabinets, built-in pantry and breakfast room with menu desk and bay window
- A spacious vaulted master bedroom, two secondary bedrooms with bath and loft area adorn the second floor
- 3 bedrooms, 2 1/2 baths, 2-car garage with storage area
- Basement foundation

Price Code C

Second Floor
1,000 sq. ft.

First Floor
977 sq. ft.

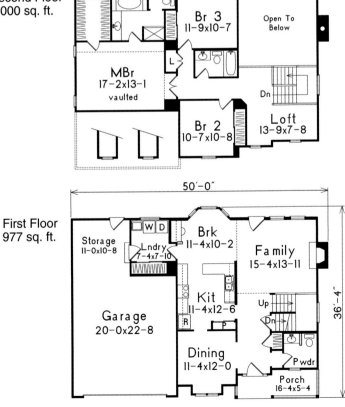

To order this plan, visit the Menards Building Materials Desk.

91

Lakehaven

Sunken Rooms Create Exciting Spaces

1,687 total square feet of living area

Special features

- Entry leads to a step-down sunken great room with a vaulted ceiling, stone fireplace, wet bar and large dining room
- Six windows wrap around the spacious U-shaped kitchen for spectacular views
- The master bedroom suite features lots of closet space, windows wrapping the tub and access to the rear patio
- 2 bedrooms, 2 baths, 1-car garage
- Crawl space foundation

Price Code B

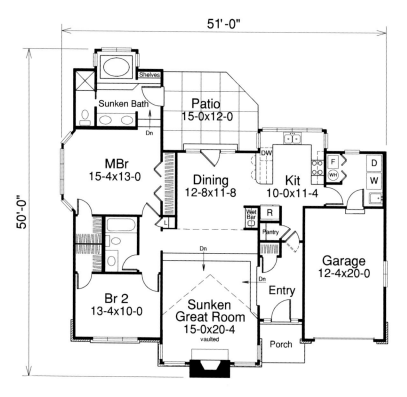

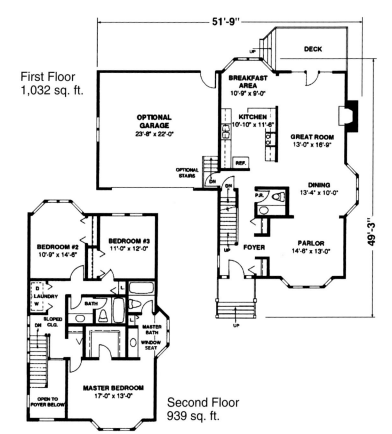

First Floor
1,032 sq. ft.

51'-9"

DECK

UP

BREAKFAST AREA
10'-9" x 9'-0"

OPTIONAL GARAGE
23'-8" x 22'-0"

KITCHEN
10'-10" x 11'-6"

GREAT ROOM
13'-0" x 16'-9"

REF.

OPTIONAL STAIRS

DN

DINING
13'-4" x 10'-0"

P.R.

PARLOR
14'-6" x 13'-0"

UP

FOYER

UP

49'-3"

BEDROOM #2
10'-9" x 14'-6"

BEDROOM #3
11'-0" x 12'-0"

D
LAUNDRY
W

BATH

SLOPED CLG.

MASTER BATH

DN

WINDOW SEAT

OPEN TO FOYER BELOW

MASTER BEDROOM
17'-0" x 13'-0"

Second Floor
939 sq. ft.

Woodbine

Wonderful Victorian Styling

1,971 total square feet of living area

Special features

- Great room, kitchen and breakfast area unite to provide a central living space
- Unique parlor offers place for conversation off the dining area
- Deluxe master bedroom has a walk-in closet and sunny master bath
- 3 bedrooms, 2 1/2 baths, optional 2-car garage
- Basement foundation

Price Code C

Bellerive

Soaring Covered Portico

2,056 total square feet of living area

Special features

- Columned foyer projects past the living and dining rooms into the family room
- Kitchen conveniently accesses the dining room and breakfast area
- Master bedroom features double-door access to the patio and a pocket door to the private bath with walk-in closet, double-bowl vanity and tub
- 4 bedrooms, 2 baths, 2-car garage
- Slab foundation, drawings also include crawl space foundation

Price Code C

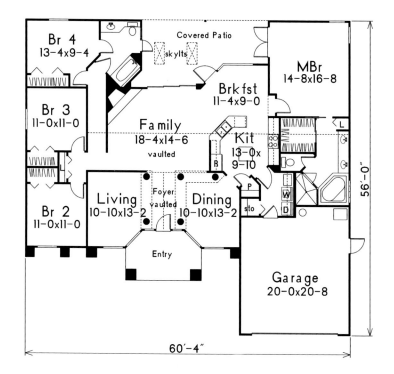

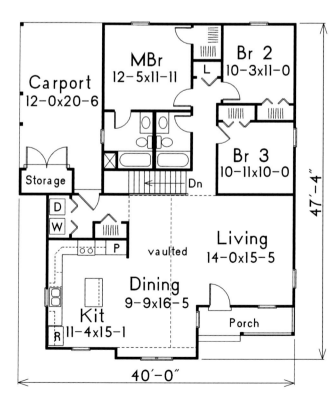

Franklin

Compact Home With Funtional Design

1,396 total square feet of living area

Special features

- Gabled front adds interest to the facade
- Living and dining rooms share a vaulted ceiling
- Master bedroom features a walk-in closet and private bath
- Functional kitchen boasts a center work island and convenient pantry
- 3 bedrooms, 2 baths, 1-car rear entry carport
- Basement foundation, drawings also include crawl space foundation

Price Code A

To order this plan, visit the Menards Building Materials Desk.

95

Sunwood

Capture The Sun

1,852 total square feet of living area

Special features

- Exterior appearance is heightened with the use of a covered porch, decorative octagon-shaped window and cupola
- Grand-sized living room presents itself upon entering and relishes in front and rear views
- Dining room and kitchen access a beautiful sun space immersed in light from surrounding windows
- 3 bedrooms, 2 1/2 baths, 2-car garage
- Basement foundation, drawings also include crawl space and slab foundations

Price Code C

First Floor
912 sq. ft.

Second Floor
940 sq. ft.

96

To order this plan, visit the Menards Building Materials Desk.

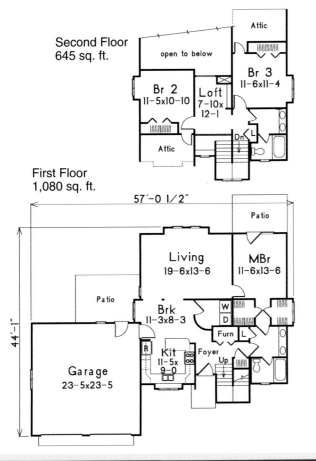

Second Floor
645 sq. ft.

Attic

open to below

Br 3
11-6x11-4

Br 2
11-5x10-10

Loft
7-10x
12-1

Dn

Attic

First Floor
1,080 sq. ft.

57'-0 1/2"

Patio

Living
19-6x13-6

MBr
11-6x13-6

Patio

Brk
11-3x8-3

W
D

Furn   L

44'-1"

Kit
11-5x
9-0

Foyer

Up

Garage
23-5x23-5

Landmark

Contemporary Home With Unique Layout

1,725 total square feet of living area

Special features
- Loft offers private niche overlooking foyer and living room
- Kitchen and breakfast rooms are separated by the breakfast bar
- Master bedroom features double walk-in closets, large vanity and private bath area
- 2" x 6" exterior walls available, please order plan #M02-001D-0115
- 3 bedrooms, 2 baths, 2-car garage
- Crawl space foundation, drawings also include basement and slab foundations

Price Code B

Westover

Compact Home, Perfect Fit For Narrow Lot

1,085 total square feet of living area

Special features

- Rear porch provides handy access through the kitchen
- Convenient hall linen closet is located on the second floor
- Breakfast bar in the kitchen offers additional counterspace
- Living and dining rooms combine for open living
- 3 bedrooms, 2 baths
- Basement foundation

Price Code AA

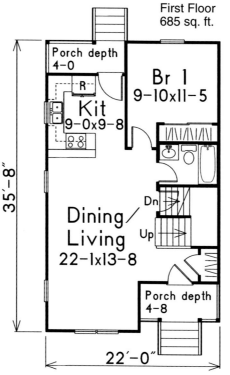

First Floor
685 sq. ft.

Porch depth
4-0

R

Kit
9-0x9-8

Br 1
9-10x11-5

Dining/
Living
22-1x13-8

Dn

Up

Porch depth
4-8

35'-8"

22'-0"

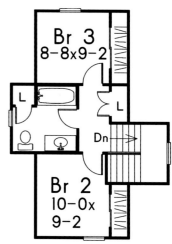

Br 3
8-8x9-2

L

L

Dn

Br 2
10-0x
9-2

Second Floor
400 sq. ft.

98

To order this plan, visit the Menards Building Materials Desk.

MENARDS®

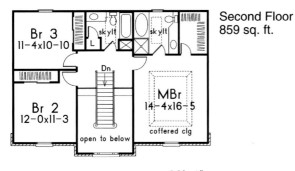

Second Floor
859 sq. ft.

Br 3
11-4x10-10

sky lt   sky lt

Dn

Br 2
12-0x11-3

MBr
14-4x16-5

open to below

coffered clg

68'-4"

Patio

27'-4"

Family
17-3x13-1

Kit/Brk
20-3x13-1

Garage
24-1x22-1

plant
shelf

Dn

Living
12-0x11-4

Dining
14-4x12-6

W D

plant
shelf

Up

Foyer

coffered clg

Porch

First Floor
1,137 sq. ft.

Stonebriar

Blends Open And Private Living Areas

1,996 total square feet of living area

Special features
- Both the master bath and second floor bath have cheerful skylights
- Family room includes a wet bar and fireplace flanked by attractive quarter round windows
- 9' ceilings throughout the first floor with plant shelving in foyer and dining area
- 3 bedrooms, 2 1/2 baths, 2-car side entry garage
- Basement foundation, drawings also include crawl space and slab foundations

Price Code C

Baronet

A Touch Of Mediterranean

1,927 total square feet of living area

Special features

- Symmetry creates plenty of curb appeal to the front facade of this home
- Large living room features a cozy fireplace and views into the dining area with a wide bay window
- A smartly designed kitchen has all the amenities and opens to an expansive family room with fireplace
- Second floor enjoys an exquisite master bedroom and has convenient laundry facilities
- 3 bedrooms, 2 1/2 baths, 2-car garage
- Crawl space foundation

Price Code C

Second Floor
943 sq. ft.

MASTER BATH

LAUNDRY AREA

BATH

BEDROOM
12'-0" x 12'-0"

DN.

MASTER BEDROOM
19'-0" x 14'-0"

OPEN BELOW

BEDROOM
12'-0" x 13'-0"

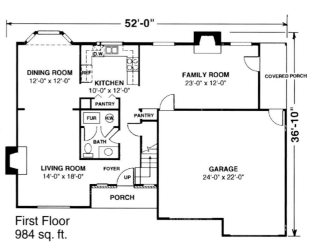

52'-0"

DINING ROOM
12'-0" x 12'-0"

D.W.

REF

KITCHEN
10'-0" x 12'-0"

FAMILY ROOM
23'-0" x 12'-0"

COVERED PORCH

PANTRY

FUR

H.W.

PANTRY

BATH

36'-10"

LIVING ROOM
14'-0" x 18'-0"

FOYER

UP

PORCH

GARAGE
24'-0" x 22'-0"

First Floor
984 sq. ft.

100

To order this plan, visit the Menards Building Materials Desk.

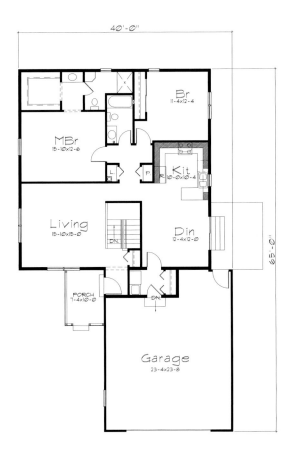

Gordon

Stylish And Efficient Ranch

1,366 total square feet of living area

Special features

- Energy efficient home with 2" x 6" exterior walls
- A delightful front porch opens into the roomy living area, perfect for family gatherings
- The kitchen features a wrap-around counter connecting to the dining room that enjoys access to the backyard
- Relax in the master bedroom suite that offers a private bath, dressing area and walk-in closet
- 2 bedrooms, 2 baths, 2-car garage
- Basement foundation

Price Code A

To order this plan, visit the Menards Building Materials Desk.

101

Meadowview

Inviting Porches On All Sides

1,618 total square feet of living area

Special features

- Wrap-around porch offers a covered passageway to the garage
- Dramatic two-story entry, with balcony above and staircase provide an expansive feel with an added decorative oval window
- Dazzling kitchen features walk-in pantry, convenient laundry and covered rear porch
- 3 bedrooms, 2 1/2 baths, 1-car garage
- Basement foundation

Price Code B

Second Floor
754 sq. ft.

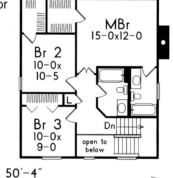

MBr
15-0x12-0

Br 2
10-0x
10-5

Br 3
10-0x
9-0

open to
below

Dn

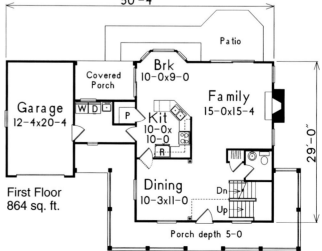

50'-4"

Patio

Covered
Porch

Brk
10-0x9-0

Family
15-0x15-4

Garage
12-4x20-4

W D

P

Kit
10-0x
10-0

R

29'-0"

Dining
10-3x11-0

Dn

Up

First Floor
864 sq. ft.

Porch depth 5-0

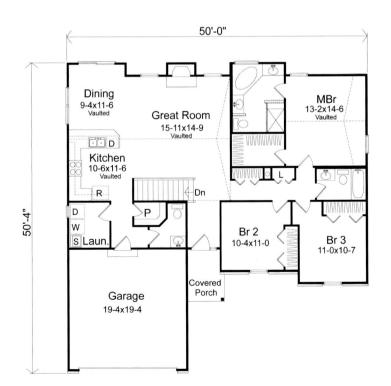

New Haven

Vaulted Great Room

1,568 total square feet of living area

Special features

- Family and friends will love to gather around the kitchen snack bar that is open to the dining and great rooms
- A half bath, walk-in pantry and laundry area at the garage entrance adds simplicity to family functions
- A vaulted ceiling crowns the master bedroom, and the deluxe bath makes this area a luxurious suite
- 3 bedrooms, 2 1/2 baths, 2-car garage
- Basement foundation

Price Code AA

Fieldcrest

Split Entry With Lots Of Room For Future Growth

1,803 total square feet of living area

Special features

- Master bedroom features a raised ceiling and private bath with a walk-in closet, large double-bowl vanity and separate tub and shower
- U-shaped kitchen includes a corner sink and convenient pantry
- Vaulted living room is complete with a fireplace and built-in cabinet
- 3 bedrooms, 2 baths, 3-car drive under garage
- Basement foundation

Price Code C

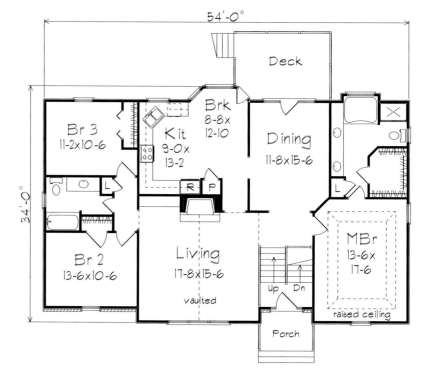

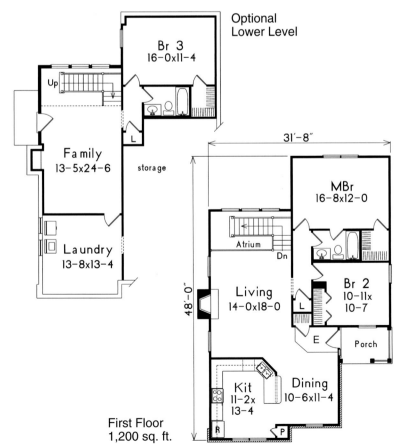

Optional Lower Level

Br 3
16-0x11-4

Up

storage

Family
13-5x24-6

Laundry
13-8x13-4

31'-8"

MBr
16-8x12-0

Atrium

Dn

Living
14-0x18-0

Br 2
10-11x
10-7

48'-0"

E

Porch

Kit
11-2x
13-4

Dining
10-6x11-4

R

P

First Floor
1,200 sq. ft.

Thornberry

Exciting Living For A Narrow Sloping Lot

1,200 total square feet of living area

Special features

- Entry leads to a large dining area which opens to the kitchen and sun-drenched living room
- An expansive window wall in the two-story atrium lends space and light to living room with fireplace
- The large kitchen features a breakfast bar and storage galore
- 697 square feet of optional living area on the lower level includes a family room, bedroom #3 and a bath
- 2 bedrooms, 1 bath
- Walk-out basement foundation

Price Code A

To order this plan, visit the Menards Building Materials Desk.

105

Charlemagne

Window Brightens Living Room

1,865 total square feet of living area

Special features

- The family room, breakfast area and kitchen combine forming a large open area for family activities
- A double-door entry leads to the grand master bedroom which includes two walk-in closets and a private bath
- Bedrooms #2 and #3 enjoy walk-in closets and share a bath
- 3 bedrooms, 2 1/2 baths, 2-car garage
- Basement foundation

Price Code C

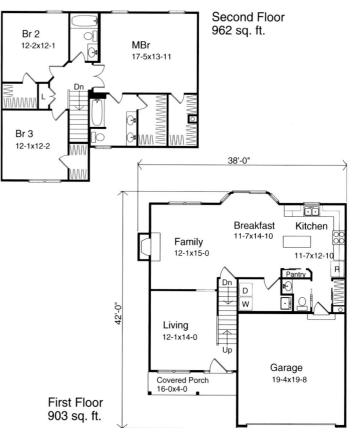

Second Floor
962 sq. ft.

Br 2
12-2x12-1

MBr
17-5x13-11

Dn

Br 3
12-1x12-2

38'-0"

Family
12-1x15-0

Breakfast
11-7x14-10

Kitchen
11-7x12-10

Pantry

Dn

D

W

R

Living
12-1x14-0

Up

42'-0"

Covered Porch
16-0x4-0

Garage
19-4x19-8

First Floor
903 sq. ft.

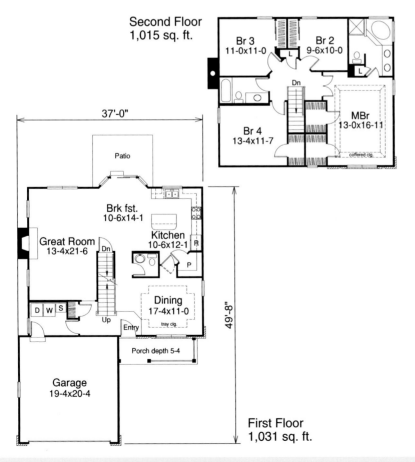

Second Floor
1,015 sq. ft.

Br 3
11-0x11-0

Br 2
9-6x10-0

Dn

MBr
13-0x16-11

Br 4
13-4x11-7

coffered clg.

37'-0"

Patio

Brk fst.
10-6x14-1

Great Room
13-4x21-6

Kitchen
10-6x12-1

Dn

R

P

D W S

Up

Dining
17-4x11-0

tray clg.

Entry

49'-8"

Porch depth 5-4

Garage
19-4x20-4

First Floor
1,031 sq. ft.

St. Charles

Classy Two-Story Perfectly Suited For A Narrow Lot

2,046 total square feet of living area

Special features

- Hipped roof and special brickwork provide nice curb appeal
- Kitchen/breakfast room offers island cabinetry, walk-in pantry, wide bay window and easy access to a large dining room
- Cheery transom windows and fireplace are just two amenities of the huge great room
- 4 bedrooms, 2 1/2 baths, 2-car garage
- Basement foundation

Price Code C

To order this plan, visit the Menards Building Materials Desk.

107

Linden

Angled Porch Greets Guests

2,059 total square feet of living area

Special features

- Large desk and pantry add to the breakfast room
- The laundry room is located on the second floor near the bedrooms
- Vaulted ceiling in the master bedroom
- Mud room is conveniently located near the garage
- 3 bedrooms, 2 1/2 baths, 2-car garage
- Basement foundation

Price Code C

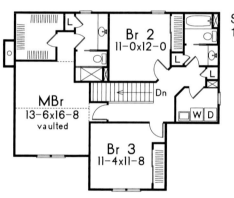

Second Floor
1,016 sq. ft.

Br 2
11-0x12-0

MBr
13-6x16-8
vaulted

Br 3
11-4x11-8

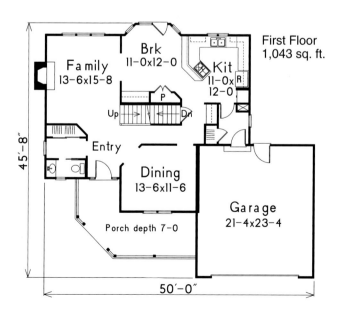

First Floor
1,043 sq. ft.

Brk
11-0x12-0

Family
13-6x15-8

Kit
11-0x
12-0

Entry

Dining
13-6x11-6

Garage
21-4x23-4

Porch depth 7-0

45'-8"

50'-0"

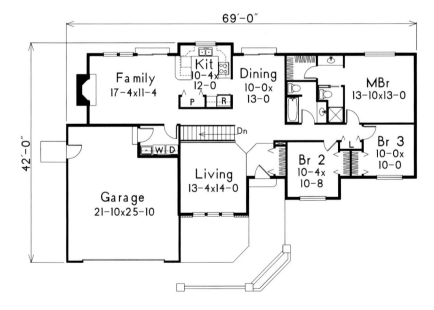

Quincy

Circle-Top Transom Window Graces This Exterior

1,588 total square feet of living area

Special features

- Energy efficient home with 2" x 6" exterior walls
- Angled walkway leads guests by an attractive landscape area
- Master bedroom has a dressing area, walk-in closet and private bath
- Sunken living room features an attractive railing on two sides
- U-shaped kitchen has a large pantry
- 3 bedrooms, 2 baths, 2-car garage
- Basement foundation, drawings also include crawl space and slab foundations

Price Code B

Middleton

Open Living Areas Separate Remote Bedrooms

1,868 total square feet of living area

Special features

- Energy efficient home with 2" x 6" exterior walls
- Dining room is surrounded by a series of arched openings which complement the open feeling of this design
- Living room has a 12' ceiling accented by skylights and a large fireplace flanked by sliding doors
- Large storage areas
- 3 bedrooms, 2 baths, 2-car side entry garage
- Slab foundation, drawings also include crawl space foundation

Price Code D

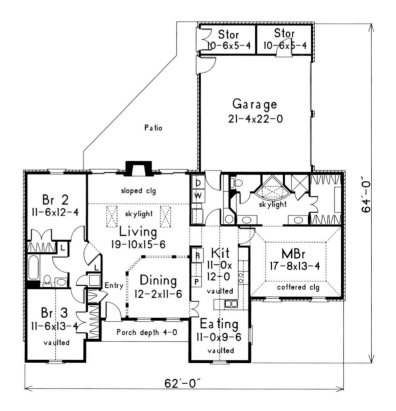

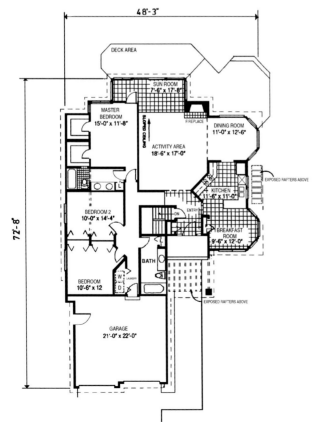

Cheswick

Handsome Contemporary Design Makes This Home Special

1,907 total square feet of living area

Special features

- Activity area amenities include a fireplace and sun room
- Formal dining area with bay windows and sliding glass doors is located at rear of kitchen
- Master bedroom has double walk-in closets and a double-vanity sink
- Two additional bedrooms share one full bath
- 3 bedrooms, 2 baths, 2-car garage
- Partial basement/crawl space foundation

Price Code C

To order this plan, visit the Menards Building Materials Desk.

111

Brayden Manor

Perfect Home For A Large Family On A Budget

1,941 total square feet of living area

Special features

■ Interesting roof lines and a spacious front porch with flanking stonework help to fashion this beautiful country home

■ The vaulted great room has a separate entry and bayed dining area suitable for a large family

■ Four additional bedrooms complete the home, one of which is ideal for a study off the great room

■ 5 bedrooms, 3 baths, 2-car side entry drive under garage

■ Walk-out basement foundation

Price Code C

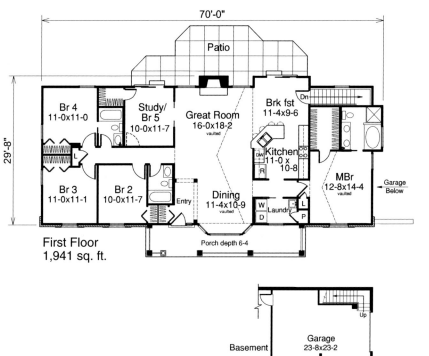

70'-0"

29'-8"

Patio

Br 4
11-0x11-0

Study/
Br 5
10-0x11-7

Great Room
16-0x18-2
vaulted

Brk fst
11-4x9-6

Dn

Kitchen
11-0 x
10-8

Br 3
11-0x11-1

Br 2
10-0x11-7

Entry

Dining
11-4x10-9
vaulted

MBr
12-8x14-4
vaulted

Garage
Below

W
D

Laundry

First Floor
1,941 sq. ft.

Porch depth 6-4

Up

Basement

Garage
23-8x23-2

Lower Level

112

To order this plan, visit the Menards Building Materials Desk.

Maryville

Grand Entryway Adorns This Home

1,941 total square feet of living area

Special features

- Energy efficient home with 2" x 6" exterior walls
- Kitchen incorporates a cooktop island, a handy pantry and adjoins the dining and family rooms
- Laundry room, half bath and closet are all located near the garage
- The dining and family rooms have access outdoors through sliding doors
- 3 bedrooms, 2 1/2 baths, 2-car garage
- Crawl space foundation

Price Code C

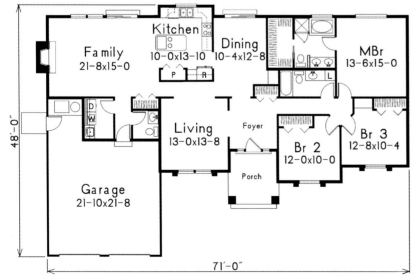

Kitchen 10-0x13-10

Family 21-8x15-0

Dining 10-4x12-8

MBr 13-6x15-0

Living 13-0x13-8

Foyer

Br 2 12-0x10-0

Br 3 12-8x10-4

Porch

Garage 21-10x21-8

48'-0"

71'-0"

To order this plan, visit the Menards Building Materials Desk.

113

Mortland

Central Fireplace Warms This Cozy Contemporary

1,442 total square feet of living area

Special features

- Centrally located living room has a recessed fireplace and 10' ceiling
- Large U-shaped kitchen offers an eating bar and pantry
- Expanded garage provides extra storage and work area
- Spacious master bedroom with sitting area and large walk-in closet
- 3 bedrooms, 2 baths, 2-car garage
- Slab foundation, drawings also include crawl space foundation

Price Code A

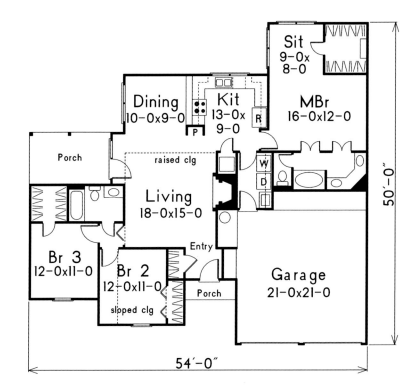

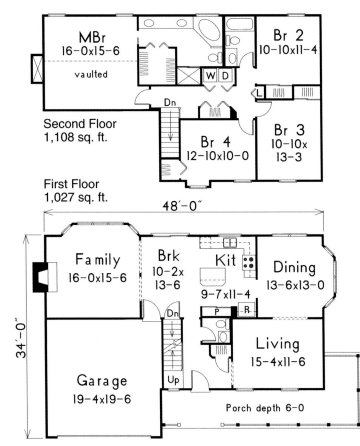

Second Floor
1,108 sq. ft.

MBr
16-0x15-6
vaulted

Br 2
10-10x11-4

W D

Br 4
12-10x10-0

Br 3
10-10x
13-3

Dn

First Floor
1,027 sq. ft.

48'-0"

34'-0"

Family
16-0x15-6

Brk
10-2x
13-6

Kit
9-7x11-4

Dining
13-6x13-0

Dn

P   R

Living
15-4x11-6

Up

Garage
19-4x19-6

Porch depth 6-0

Hermitage

Open Breakfast/ Family Room Combination

2,135 total square feet of living area

Special features

- Family room features extra space, an impressive fireplace and full wall of windows that joins the breakfast room creating a spacious entertainment area
- Washer and dryer are conveniently located on the second floor near the bedrooms
- The kitchen features an island counter and pantry
- 4 bedrooms, 2 1/2 baths, 2-car garage
- Basement foundation

Price Code D

Ivy

Farmhouse Style Offers Great Privacy

1,805 total square feet of living area

Special features

- Energy efficient home with 2" x 6" exterior walls
- Master bedroom forms its own wing
- Second floor bedrooms share a hall bath
- Large great room with fireplace blends into the formal dining room
- 3 bedrooms, 2 1/2 baths, 2-car side entry garage
- Basement foundation, drawings also include slab foundation

Price Code D

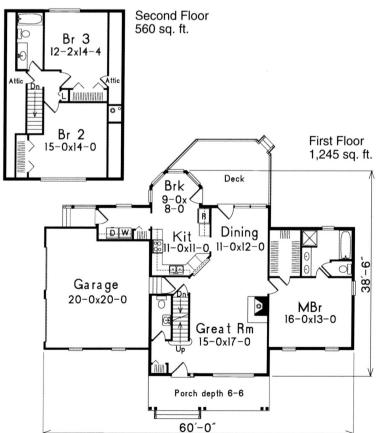

Second Floor
560 sq. ft.

Br 3
12-2x14-4

Attic   Attic

Dn

Br 2
15-0x14-0

First Floor
1,245 sq. ft.

Deck

Brk
9-0x
8-0

Kit
11-0x11-0

Dining
11-0x12-0

Garage
20-0x20-0

Dn

MBr
16-0x13-0

Great Rm
15-0x17-0

Up

Porch depth 6-6

60'-0"

38'-6"

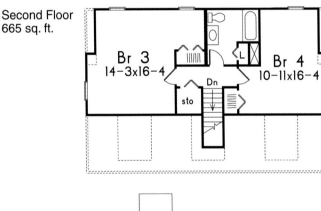

Second Floor
665 sq. ft.

Br 3
14-3x16-4

Br 4
10-11x16-4

Dn

sto

First Floor
1,040 sq. ft.

26'-0"

Dining
9-5x
9-3

Kit
10-4x9-3

R

Br 2
10-11x10-4

F

W D

Living
18-7x15-10

Br 1
14-7x12-4

Up

40'-0"

Hatteras I

Plenty Of Room For The Growing Family

1,705 total square feet of living area

Special features

- Two bedrooms on the first floor for convenience and two bedrooms on the second for privacy
- L-shaped kitchen adjacent to dining room accesses the outdoors
- First floor laundry area
- 2" x 6" exterior walls available, please order plan #M02-001D-0110
- 4 bedrooms, 2 baths
- Crawl space foundation, drawings also include basement and slab foundations

Price Code B

To order this plan, visit the Menards Building Materials Desk.

117

Southland

Home Embodies Charm Inside And Out

2,155 total square feet of living area

Special features

- Delightful family room embraces both the front and rear including a cozy fireplace and stairs to a studio above garage
- An L-shaped kitchen to the rear, enjoys a bay window
- Optional studio above garage has an additional 349 square feet of living area
- 4 bedrooms, 3 baths, 2-car garage
- Partial basement/crawl space foundation, drawings also include crawl space and slab foundations

Price Code C

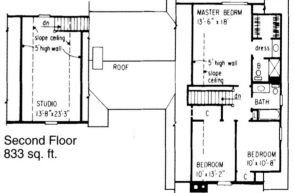

Second Floor
833 sq. ft.

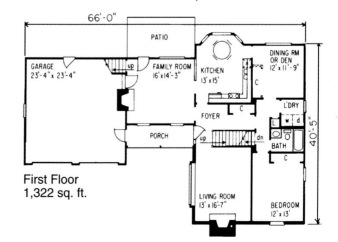

First Floor
1,322 sq. ft.

118

To order this plan, visit the Menards Building Materials Desk.

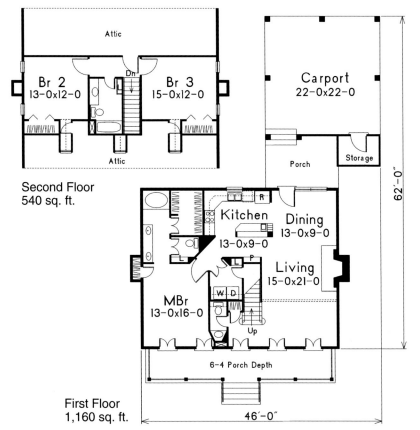

Second Floor
540 sq. ft.

Attic

Br 2
13-0x12-0

Dn

Br 3
15-0x12-0

Attic

Carport
22-0x22-0

Porch

Storage

Kitchen
13-0x9-0

Dining
13-0x9-0

Living
15-0x21-0

MBr
13-0x16-0

W D

P

Up

62'-0"

6-4 Porch Depth

First Floor
1,160 sq. ft.

46'-0"

Georgetown

Stucco Finish And Authentic Southern Home Styling

1,700 total square feet of living area

Special features

- Energy efficient home with 2" x 6" exterior walls
- Fully appointed kitchen with wet bar
- Linen drop from the second floor bath to utility room
- Master bath includes raised marble tub and a sloped ceiling
- 3 bedrooms, 2 1/2 baths, 2-car attached carport
- Crawl space foundation, drawings also include basement and slab foundations

Price Code B

Whitney

Affordable Home Features Five Bedrooms

2,012 total square feet of living area

Special features

- Gables, cantilevers, and box-bay windows all contribute to an elegant exterior
- Two-story entry leads to an efficient kitchen and bayed breakfast area with morning room
- Garage contains extra space for a shop, bicycles and miscellaneous storage
- 5 bedrooms, 2 1/2 baths, 2-car garage
- Basement foundation

Price Code C

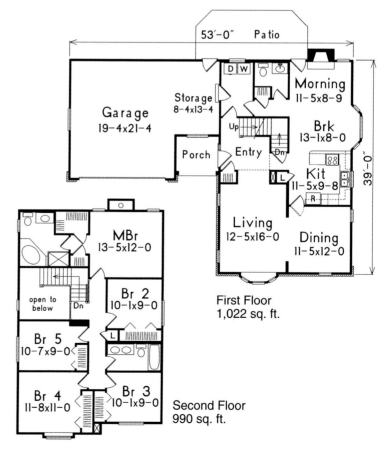

First Floor
1,022 sq. ft.

53'-0" Patio

Garage 19-4x21-4
Storage 8-4x13-4
Morning 11-5x8-9
Brk 13-1x8-0
Kit 11-5x9-8
Living 12-5x16-0
Dining 11-5x12-0
Porch
Entry
39'-0"

Second Floor
990 sq. ft.

MBr 13-5x12-0
Br 2 10-1x9-0
Br 5 10-7x9-0
Br 4 11-8x11-0
Br 3 10-1x9-0
open to below

120

To order this plan, visit the Menards Building Materials Desk.

First Floor
1,207 sq. ft.

44'-0"

32'-0"

MBr
13-5x11-11

Brkfst/Kit
19-0x10-0
Vaulted

P

L

Dn

Family
13-5x15-11
Vaulted

Br 2
10-0x11-0

Br 3
10-1x11-0

Dn

W W D

F

Garage
20x26-9

Basement
20x27

Lower Level

Oaklawn

Cozy Split Level

1,207 total square feet of living area

Special features

- A bay window with access to the outdoors, pantry and island with seating enhance the kitchen/breakfast area
- A vaulted ceiling and fireplace add elegance to the family room
- Bedrooms are separated from main living areas for privacy
- 3 bedrooms, 2 baths, 2-car garage
- Basement foundation

Price Code A

Davenport

Impressive Corner Fireplace Highlights The Living Area

1,458 total square feet of living area

Special features

- Convenient snack bar joins kitchen with breakfast room
- Large living room has a fireplace, plenty of windows, vaulted ceiling and nearby plant shelf
- Corner windows provide abundant light in the breakfast room
- 3 bedrooms, 2 baths, 2-car garage
- Crawl space foundation, drawings also include slab foundation

Price Code A

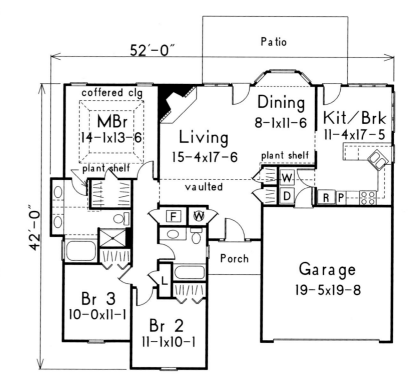

Patio

52'-0"

42'-0"

coffered clg

MBr
14-1x13-6

plant shelf

Living
15-4x17-6

vaulted

Dining
8-1x11-6

Kit/Brk
11-4x17-5

plant shelf

W
D

F W

R P

Br 3
10-0x11-1

L

Br 2
11-1x10-1

Porch

Garage
19-5x19-8

122

To order this plan, visit the Menards Building Materials Desk.

Glencoe

Gracious Living On A Small Lot

1,671 total square feet of living area

Special features

- Triple gables and stone facade create great curb appeal
- Two-story entry with hallway leads to a spacious family room, dining area with bay window and U-shaped kitchen
- Second floor features a large master bedroom with luxury bath, huge walk-in closet, overlook to entry and two secondary bedrooms with hall bath
- 3 bedrooms, 2 1/2 baths, 2-car garage
- Basement foundation

Price Code B

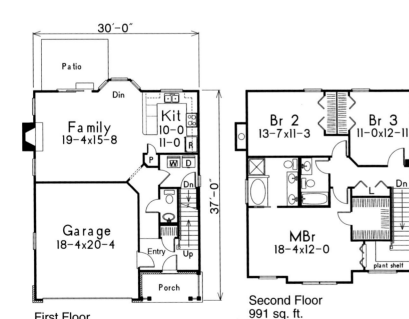

First Floor
680 sq. ft.

Second Floor
991 sq. ft.

Mardel

Charming Two-Story Traditional

2,174 total square feet of living area

Special features

- The first floor features 9' ceilings
- The bayed breakfast area includes a built-in desk, pantry and access to the outdoors
- The master bedroom enjoys an abundance of storage space with two large walk-in closets
- The laundry area is conveniently located near the bedrooms
- 3 bedrooms, 2 1/2 baths, 2-car side entry garage
- Basement foundation

Price Code C

Second Floor
1,091 sq. ft.

MBr
13-8x17-1

Br 2
11-1x12-1

Br 3
11-3x12-4

First Floor
1,083 sq. ft.

52'-0"

46'-0"

Family
13-8x15-8

Brkfst
13-0x11-11

Kit.
12-4x11-11

Mud Rm

Dining
13-8x12-4

Porch
14-0x5-8

Garage
21-0x23-4

124

To order this plan, visit the Menards Building Materials Desk.

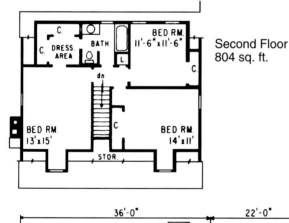

**Second Floor
804 sq. ft.**

BED RM.
11'-6" x 11'-6"

C.

DRESS.
AREA

BATH

C.

C.

dn

BED RM.
13' x 15'

C

BED RM.
14' x 11'

STOR.

**First Floor
1,068 sq. ft.**

36'-0"

22'-0"

PATIO

KIT.
10'-10" x 12'

DW.

MUD
RM.

D.

W.

FAMILY RM.
16'-2" x 12'

dn

DINE

C.

30'-8"

WALK-
IN
CLO.

BATH

21'-7" x 21'-2"

C

FOYER

LIVING RM.
13' x 17'-5"

up

BED RM.
OR
DINING
13' x 12'

Rutherford

Design Has Traditional Elegance

1,872 total square feet of living area

Special features

- Recessed porch has entry door with sidelights and roof dormers adding charm
- First floor bedroom has access to bath and laundry room making it perfect for the master bedroom or a live-in parent
- Largest of three second floor bedrooms enjoys double closets and private access to hall bath
- 4 bedrooms, 2 baths, 2-car garage
- Basement foundation, drawings also include crawl space and slab foundations

Price Code C

Oakbriar

Vaulted Ceilings Highlight This Home

1,560 total square feet of living area

Special features

- Cozy breakfast room is tucked at the rear of this home and features plenty of windows for natural light
- Large entry has easy access to the secondary bedrooms, utility area, and dining and living rooms
- Private master bedroom
- Kitchen overlooks the living room which features a fireplace and patio access
- 3 bedrooms, 2 baths, 2-car garage
- Slab foundation

Price Code B

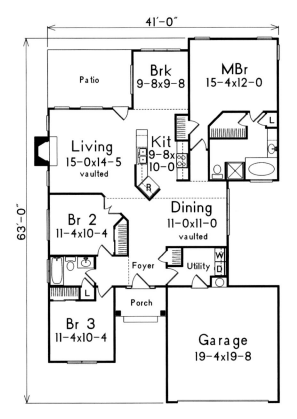

126

To order this plan, visit the Menards Building Materials Desk.

Second Floor
677 sq. ft.

MBr
11-8x14-0

Loft
9-0x
12-6

Br 2
10-0x
14-0

Dn

open to below

vaulted

48'-0"

Deck

Garage
19-8x23-4

Kit
10-4x11-0

Dining
11-0x13-4

Dn

R

Living
18-0x12-8
vaulted

Up

29'-10"

First Floor
674 sq. ft.

Wintergreen

Tall Windows, Sweeping Roof Lines Make A Sizable Impression

1,351 total square feet of living area

Special features

- Roof lines and vaulted ceilings make this home appear larger
- Central fireplace provides a focal point for the dining and living areas
- Master bedroom features a roomy window seat and a walk-in closet
- Loft can easily be converted to a third bedroom
- 2 bedrooms, 2 1/2 baths, 2-car garage
- Basement foundation

Price Code A

Scottfield

Compact And Convenient Farmhouse

1,958 total square feet of living area

Special features

- Spacious kitchen and breakfast area is open to the rear deck
- A charming rail separates the family room and breakfast area keeping an open feel
- Dormers add interest and spaciousness in bedroom #2
- Bonus room on the second floor is included in the square footage
- 3 bedrooms, 2 1/2 baths, 2-car side entry garage
- Basement foundation, drawings also include slab and crawl space foundations

Price Code D

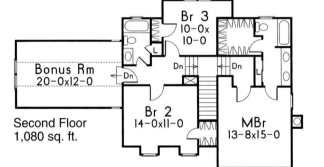

Second Floor
1,080 sq. ft.

Br 3
10-0x
10-0

Bonus Rm
20-0x12-0

Br 2
14-0x11-0

MBr
13-8x15-0

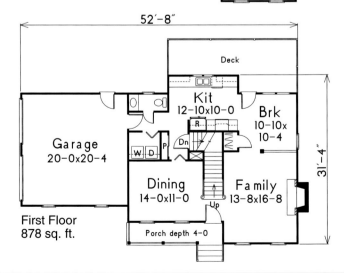

52'-8"

Deck

Kit
12-10x10-0

Brk
10-10x
10-4

Garage
20-0x20-4

Dining
14-0x11-0

Family
13-8x16-8

31'-4"

First Floor
878 sq. ft.

Porch depth 4-0

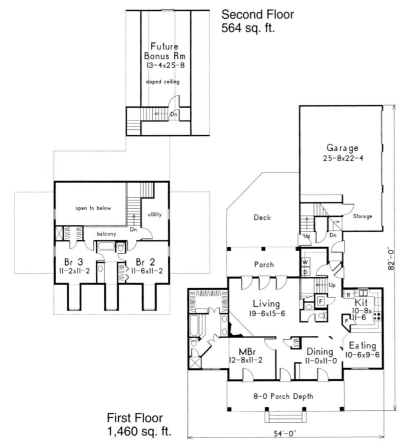

Second Floor
564 sq. ft.

Future
Bonus Rm
13-4x25-8

sloped ceiling

On

open to below

utility

balcony

Dn

Br 3
11-2x11-2

Br 2
11-6x11-2

Garage
25-8x22-4

Deck

Storage

Up

Dn

Porch

W
D

Up

Living
19-6x15-6

F

Kit
10-8x
11-6

R

P

MBr
12-8x11-2

Dining
11-0x11-0

Eating
10-6x9-6

8-0 Porch Depth

First Floor
1,460 sq. ft.

82'-0"

54'-0"

Dougherty

Distinctive Front Facade With Generous Porch

2,024 total square feet of living area

Special features

- Energy efficient home with 2" x 6" exterior walls
- Living room features a fireplace, access to the covered rear porch, 18' ceiling and a balcony
- Closet for handling recyclables
- Future bonus room has an additional 475 square feet of living area
- 3 bedrooms, 2 1/2 baths, 2-car side entry garage
- Crawl space foundation, drawings also include slab and basement foundations

Price Code C

Ardmore

Open Living Spaces Create Comfortable Living

1,996 total square feet of living area

Special features

- Centrally located activity area has a fireplace and double sliding glass doors accessing the covered patio with skylights
- Spacious master bedroom includes a private bath with skylight and walk-in closets
- Private nook with a double-door entry makes an ideal office area
- 2 bedrooms, 2 baths, 2-car side entry carport
- Slab foundation

Price Code C

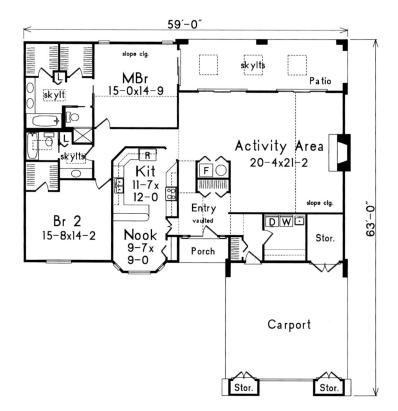

59'-0"

63'-0"

slope clg.

MBr
15-0x14-9

skylt

skylt

skylts

Patio

Activity Area
20-4x21-2

slope clg.

Kit
11-7x
12-0

R

F

Entry
vaulted

D W

Stor.

Br 2
15-8x14-2

Nook
9-7x
9-0

Porch

Carport

Stor.   Stor.

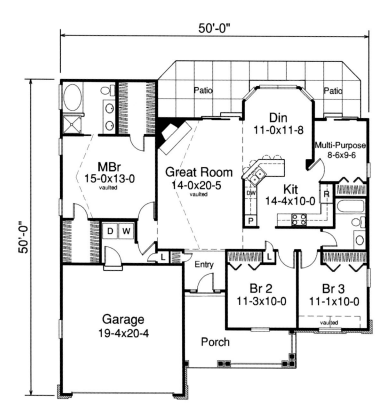

50'-0"

50'-0"

Patio

Patio

Din
11-0x11-8

Multi-Purpose
8-6x9-6

MBr
15-0x13-0
vaulted

Great Room
14-0x20-5
vaulted

Kit
14-4x10-0

D W

D/W

P

R

L

Entry

L

L

Br 2
11-3x10-0

Br 3
11-1x10-0
vaulted

Garage
19-4x20-4

Porch

Ashmont Park

Elegance With Efficiency

1,580 total square feet of living area

Special features

- Home offers great looks with an oversized front porch
- The large great room features a corner fireplace, vaulted ceiling, and access to the patio
- The spacious kitchen enjoys an adjoining multi-purpose room ideal for a study or hobby room
- The master bedroom has a vaulted ceiling and two walk-in closets
- 3 bedrooms, 2 baths, 2-car garage
- Crawl space foundation, drawings also include slab and basement foundations

Price Code B

Wedgegrove

Victorian Style With Double Bays

2,066 total square feet of living area

Special features

■ Large master bedroom includes sitting area and private bath

■ Open living room features a fireplace with built-in bookshelves

■ Spacious kitchen accesses formal dining area and breakfast room

■ 3 bedrooms, 2 1/2 baths, optional 2-car side entry garage

■ Slab foundation

Price Code C

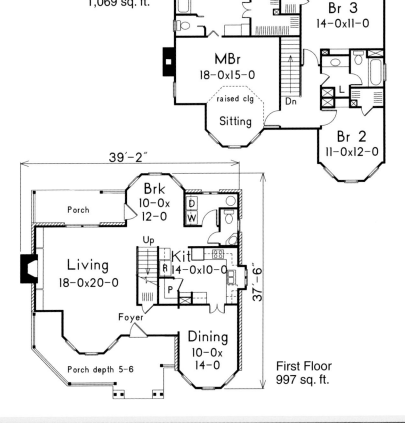

Second Floor 1,069 sq. ft.

Br 3 14-0x11-0

MBr 18-0x15-0

raised clg

Sitting

Dn

Br 2 11-0x12-0

39'-2"

37'-6"

Brk 10-0x 12-0

Porch

D W

Up

Kit 14-0x10-0

R

Living 18-0x20-0

P

Foyer

Dining 10-0x 14-0

Porch depth 5-6

First Floor 997 sq. ft.

132

To order this plan, visit the Menards Building Materials Desk.

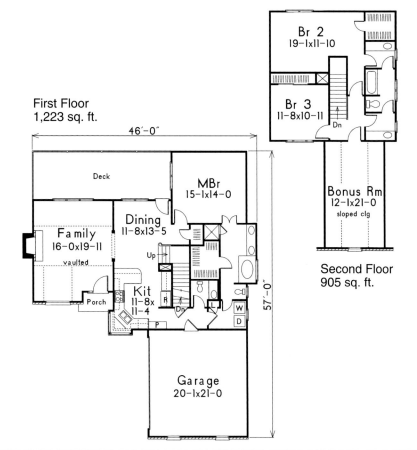

First Floor
1,223 sq. ft.

46'-0"

Deck

MBr
15-1x14-0

Family
16-0x19-11
vaulted

Dining
11-8x13-5

Up

Kit
11-8x
11-4

Porch

R

Dn

W
D

L

P

57'-0"

Garage
20-1x21-0

Br 2
19-1x11-10

Br 3
11-8x10-11

Dn

Bonus Rm
12-1x21-0
sloped clg

Second Floor
905 sq. ft.

Fulton

Charming With Many Gables

2,128 total square feet of living area

Special features

- Large bonus area over the garage, which is included in the square footage, converts to a fourth bedroom or activity center
- Family room fireplace and vaulted ceiling provide an attractive entry
- Master bedroom features a bath with windowed tub, walk-in closet, separate shower and plenty of storage space
- 3 bedrooms, 2 1/2 baths, 2-car side entry garage
- Basement foundation

Price Code C

Lamont

Breakfast Nook Fits In Cozy Bay

2,045 total square feet of living area

Special features

- Master bedroom includes a walk-in closet and private bath with corner tub and separate shower
- Both the family and breakfast rooms access the outdoors
- Two-story foyer with attractive transom windows opens into the formal living room
- 3 bedrooms, 2 1/2 baths, 2-car garage
- Basement foundation

Price Code D

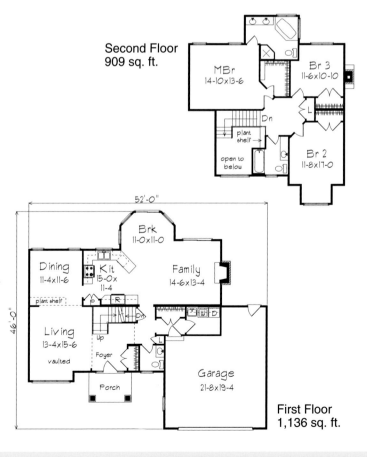

Second Floor
909 sq. ft.

MBr
14-10x13-6

Br 3
11-6x10-10

Dn

plant
shelf

open to
below

Br 2
11-8x17-0

52'-0"

46'-0"

Brk
11-0x11-0

Dining
11-4x11-6

Kit
15-0x
11-4

Family
14-6x13-4

plant shelf

Living
13-4x15-6

vaulted

Up

Foyer

Porch

Garage
21-8x19-4

First Floor
1,136 sq. ft.

Richland

Arched Accents Enhance Facade

1,704 total square feet of living area

Special features
- Open living and dining areas combine for added spaciousness
- Master bedroom features a private bath and walk-in closet
- Sunny kitchen/nook has space for dining
- Cabinet bar in hallway leading to the living area is designed for entertaining
- 3 bedrooms, 2 baths, 2-car garage
- Basement foundation

Price Code B

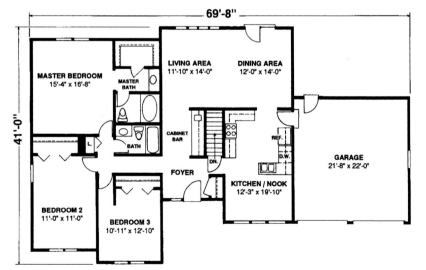

69'-8"

41'-0"

MASTER BEDROOM
15'-4" x 16'-8"

MASTER BATH

LIVING AREA
11'-10" x 14'-0"

DINING AREA
12'-0" x 14'-0"

CABINET BAR

BATH

REF.

GARAGE
21'-8" x 22'-0"

DN.

D.W.

FOYER

BEDROOM 2
11'-0" x 11'-0"

BEDROOM 3
10'-11" x 12'-10"

KITCHEN / NOOK
12'-3" x 19'-10"

To order this plan, visit the Menards Building Materials Desk.

135

Smithfield

High Ceilings Create A Feeling Of Luxury

1,707 total square feet of living area

Special features

- The formal living room off the entry hall has a high sloping ceiling and prominent fireplace
- Kitchen and breakfast area allow access to the garage and rear porch
- Master bedroom has an impressive vaulted ceiling, luxurious bath, walk-in closet and separate tub and shower
- Utility room is conveniently located near the bedrooms
- 3 bedrooms, 2 baths, 2-car garage
- Slab foundation

Price Code C

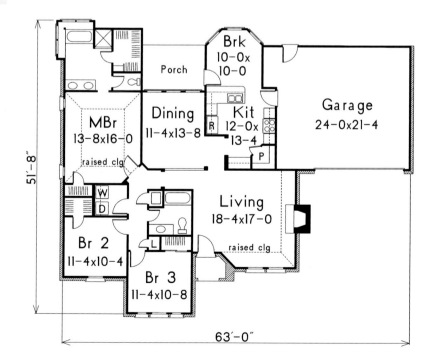

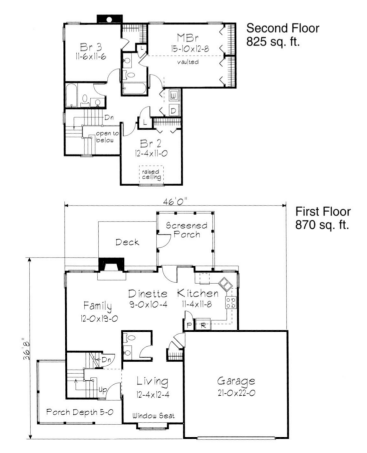

Second Floor
825 sq. ft.

Br 3
11-6x11-6

MBr
15-10x12-8
vaulted

Dn

open to
below

Br 2
12-4x11-0

raised
ceiling

46'0"

First Floor
870 sq. ft.

Deck

Screened
Porch

36'8"

Family
12-0x19-0

Dinette
9-0x10-4

Kitchen
11-4x11-8

P R

Dn

Up

Living
12-4x12-4

Garage
21-0x22-0

Porch Depth 5-0

Window Seat

Westwood

Two-Story Home With Uncommon Charm

1,695 total square feet of living area

Special features

- Facade features a cozy wrap-around porch, projected living room window and front gables
- Balcony overlooks to the entry below
- Kitchen has a full-view corner window with adjacent eating space that opens to the screened porch
- Vaulted master bedroom enjoys double closets and a private bath
- 3 bedrooms, 2 1/2 baths, 2-car garage
- Basement foundation

Price Code B

To order this plan, visit the Menards Building Materials Desk.

137

Springate

Luxurious Master Bedroom

1,587 total square feet of living area

Special features

- The spacious family room features a vaulted ceiling, fireplace and convenient coat closet
- The kitchen/breakfast area is brightened by a large window and includes a convenient pantry
- Secondary bedrooms are generously sized and share a full bath
- 3 bedrooms, 2 baths, 2-car garage
- Basement foundation

Price Code B

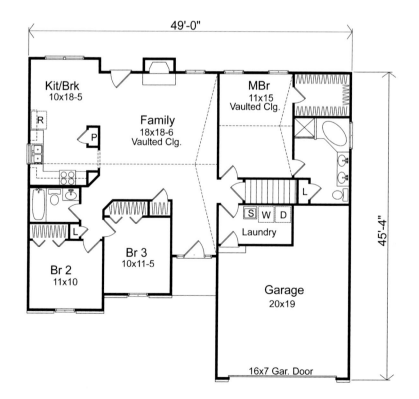

49'-0"

Kit/Brk
10x18-5

R

P

Family
18x18-6
Vaulted Clg.

MBr
11x15
Vaulted Clg.

L

S W D

Laundry

Br 3
10x11-5

Br 2
11x10

L

45'-4"

Garage
20x19

16x7 Gar. Door

138

To order this plan, visit the Menards Building Materials Desk.

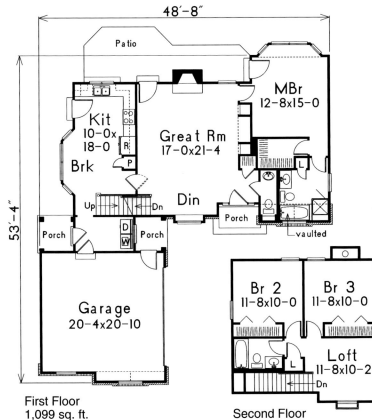

First Floor
1,099 sq. ft.

Second Floor
520 sq. ft.

Yorkshire

Prestigious Appeal For A Modest Home

1,619 total square feet of living area

Special features
- Elegant home features three quaint porches and a rear patio
- Grand-scale great room offers a dining area, fireplace with a built-in alcove and shelves for an entertainment center
- First floor master bedroom has a walk-in closet, luxury bath, bay window and access to rear patio
- Breakfast room with bay window has a staircase that leads to the second floor bedrooms and loft
- 3 bedrooms, 2 1/2 baths, 2-car side entry garage
- Basement foundation

Price Code B

Brighton

Spacious Family Room For Growing Families

2,147 total square feet of living area

Special features

- Living and dining rooms are adjacent to the entry foyer for easy access
- Kitchen is conveniently located next to the sunny breakfast nook
- Master bedroom includes a large walk-in closet and luxurious bath
- Breakfast area offers easy access to the deck
- 4 bedrooms, 2 1/2 baths, 2-car garage
- Basement foundation

Price Code C

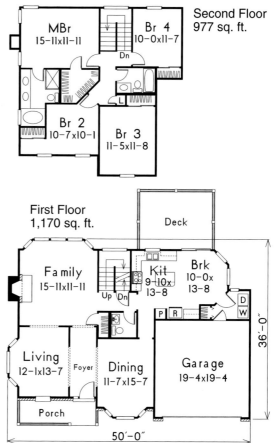

Second Floor
977 sq. ft.

MBr
15-11x11-11

Br 4
10-0x11-7

Dn

Br 2
10-7x10-1

Br 3
11-5x11-8

First Floor
1,170 sq. ft.

Deck

Family
15-11x11-11

Up Dn

Kit
9-10x
13-8

Brk
10-0x
13-8

P R

D W

Living
12-1x13-7

Foyer

Dining
11-7x15-7

Garage
19-4x19-4

Porch

36'-0"

50'-0"

Second Floor
638 sq. ft.

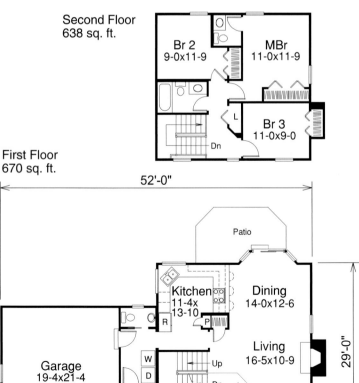

Br 2
9-0x11-9

MBr
11-0x11-9

Br 3
11-0x9-0

Dn

First Floor
670 sq. ft.

52'-0"

Patio

Kitchen
11-4x
13-10

Dining
14-0x12-6

R

P

Garage
19-4x21-4

Living
16-5x10-9

W
D

Up

Dn

29'-0"

Porch depth 5-4

Oakbrook

Affordable Two-Story Has It All

1,308 total square feet of living area

Special features

- Multi-gabled facade and elongated porch create a pleasing country appeal
- Large dining room with bay window and view to rear patio opens to a full-functional kitchen with snack bar
- An attractive U-shaped stair with hall overlook leads to the second floor
- 3 bedrooms, 1 full bath, 2 half baths, 2-car garage
- Basement foundation

Price Code A

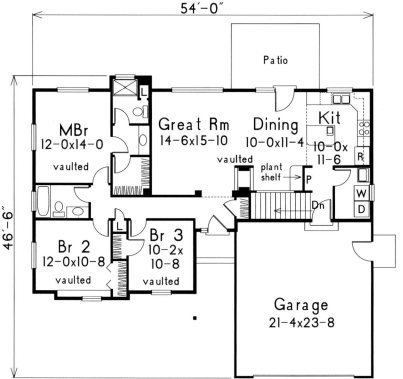

Goodwin

Vaulted Ceilings Throughout Create Dramatic Interior

1,428 total square feet of living area

Special features

- Energy efficient home with 2" x 6" exterior walls
- 10' ceilings in the entry and hallway
- Vaulted secondary bedrooms
- Kitchen is loaded with amenities including an island with salad sink and pantry
- Master bedroom with vaulted ceiling includes a large walk-in closet and private master bath
- 3 bedrooms, 2 baths, 2-car garage
- Basement foundation, drawings also include crawl space foundation

Price Code A

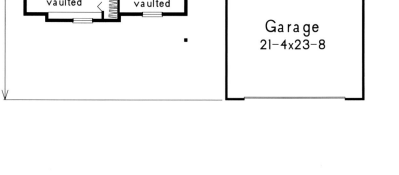

54'-0"

46'-6"

Patio

MBr
12-0x14-0
vaulted

Great Rm
14-6x15-10

Dining
10-0x11-4
vaulted

Kit
10-0x
11-6

plant shelf

P

Dn

W
D

Br 2
12-0x10-8
vaulted

Br 3
10-2x
10-8
vaulted

Garage
21-4x23-8

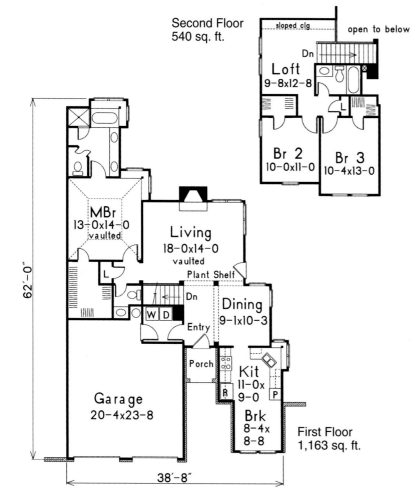

Second Floor
540 sq. ft.

sloped clg   open to below

Dn

Loft
9-8x12-8

Br 2
10-0x11-0

Br 3
10-4x13-0

MBr
13-0x14-0
vaulted

Living
18-0x14-0
vaulted

Plant Shelf

Dn

Dining
9-1x10-3

W D

Entry

Porch

Kit
11-0x
9-0

Garage
20-4x23-8

Brk
8-4x
8-8

First Floor
1,163 sq. ft.

62'-0"

38'-8"

Wistar

Corner Windows Brighten Charming 1 1/2 Story

1,703 total square feet of living area

Special features

- Large fireplace, French doors onto patio and plant shelves enhance the living room
- Protected front entry includes a raised ceiling in the foyer
- Master bedroom enjoys a walk-in closet, vaulted ceiling and window seats
- Plan is well-suited for a narrow lot
- 3 bedrooms, 2 1/2 baths, 2-car garage
- Slab foundation, drawings also include crawl space foundation

Price Code B

Hilltop

Palladian Windows Dominate Facade

1,500 total square feet of living area

Special features

- Living room features a cathedral ceiling and opens to the breakfast room
- Breakfast room has a spectacular bay window and adjoins a well-appointed kitchen with storage
- Laundry room is convenient to the kitchen and includes a large closet
- Large walk-in closet gives the master bedroom abundant storage
- 3 bedrooms, 2 baths, 2-car garage
- Basement foundation

Price Code B

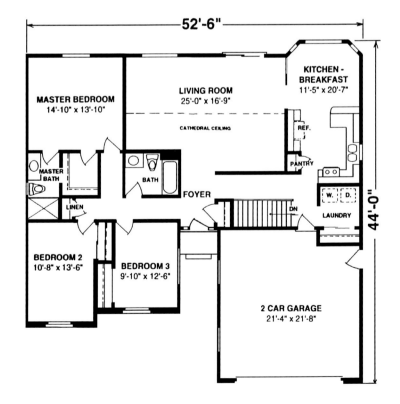

52'-6"

MASTER BEDROOM
14'-10" x 13'-10"

LIVING ROOM
25'-0" x 16'-9"

CATHEDRAL CEILING

KITCHEN - BREAKFAST
11'-5" x 20'-7"

REF.

MASTER BATH

BATH

FOYER

PANTRY

LINEN

DN

W. D.

LAUNDRY

44'-0"

BEDROOM 2
10'-8" x 13'-6"

BEDROOM 3
9'-10" x 12'-6"

2 CAR GARAGE
21'-4" x 21'-8"

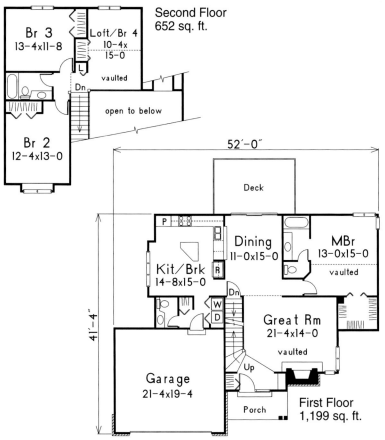

Second Floor
652 sq. ft.

Br 3
13-4x11-8

Loft/Br 4
10-4x
15-0

vaulted

Dn

open to below

Br 2
12-4x13-0

52'-0"

Deck

41'-4"

P

Dining
11-0x15-0

MBr
13-0x15-0

Kit/Brk
14-8x15-0

R

vaulted

W
D

Dn

Great Rm
21-4x14-0

vaulted

Garage
21-4x19-4

Up

Porch

First Floor
1,199 sq. ft.

Berrybrook

Vaulted Great Room With Open Entrance

1,851 total square feet of living area

Special features

- High-impact entrance to great room also leads directly to the second floor
- First floor master bedroom suite with corner window and walk-in closet
- Kitchen/breakfast room has center work island and pass-through to the dining room
- Second floor bedrooms share a bath
- 4 bedrooms, 2 1/2 baths, 2-car garage
- Basement foundation

Price Code D

Kennerly

Private Study

2,141 total square feet of living area

Special features

- A fireplace warms the adjoining great room, kitchen and breakfast area
- A covered porch provides outdoor entertaining space
- The master bedroom enjoys a coffered ceiling, two closets, a bath and a private study
- Each secondary bedroom features a walk-in closet
- 3 bedrooms, 2 1/2 baths, 3-car garage
- Basement foundation

Price Code C

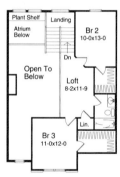

Second Floor
555 sq. ft.

Plant Shelf
Landing
Atrium Below
Br 2
10-0x13-0
Dn
Open To Below
Loft
8-2x11-9
Lin.
Br 3
11-0x12-0

50'-8"

Atrium
Landing
Up Dn
Brkfst.
10-0x10-1
Covered Porch
Coffered Clg.
Kit.
10-0x13-0
MBr
12-4x15-0
Great Rm.
16-3x15-1
3-Car/ Storage
9-8x21-8
59'-4"
Study
12-4x10-4
Dining
11-0x11-10
Porch
17-0x5-8
Garage

First Floor
1,586 sq. ft.

Bentley

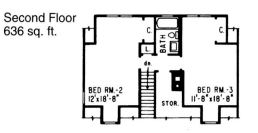

Second Floor
636 sq. ft.

BED RM.-2
12'x18'-8"

BATH

BED RM.-3
11'-8"x18'-8"

STOR.

Timeless Design Offers Prestige

1,973 total square feet of living area

Special features

- This country colonial offers a grand-sized living room
- Living room features a cozy fireplace and accesses the master bedroom complete with a walk-in closet and compartmented bath
- Laundry room with half bath and coat closet is convenient to the garage
- 3 bedrooms, 2 1/2 baths, 2-car garage
- Partial basement/crawl space foundation

Price Code C

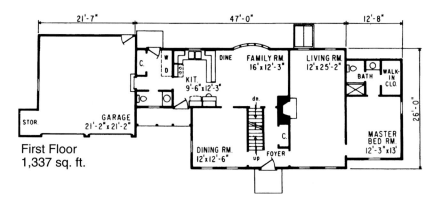

First Floor
1,337 sq. ft.

STOR.

GARAGE
21'-2"x21'-2"

KIT.
9'-6"x12'-3"

DINE

FAMILY RM.
16'x12'-3"

LIVING RM.
12'x25'-2"

BATH

WALK-IN CLO.

DINING RM.
12'x12'-6"

FOYER
up

MASTER BED RM.
12'-3"x13'

21'-7"   47'-0"   12'-8"

26'-0"

Northland

Perfect Fit For A Narrow Site

1,270 total square feet of living area

Special features

- Spacious living area features angled stairs, vaulted ceiling, exciting fireplace and deck access
- Master bedroom includes a walk-in closet and private bath
- Dining and living rooms join to create an open atmosphere
- Eat-in kitchen has a convenient pass-through to the dining room
- 3 bedrooms, 2 baths, 2-car garage
- Basement foundation

Price Code A

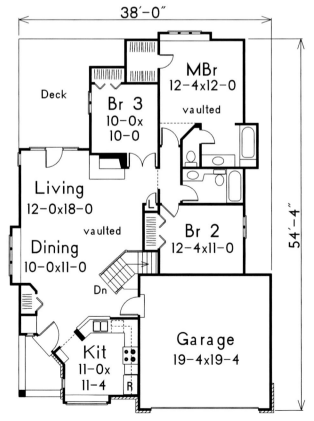

To order this plan, visit the Menards Building Materials Desk.

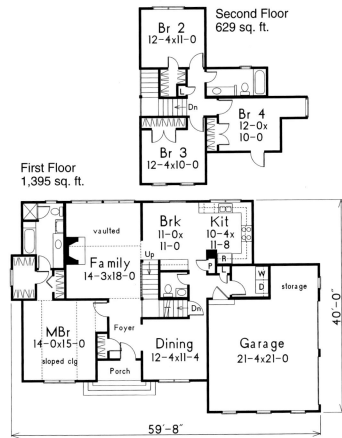

Second Floor
629 sq. ft.

Br 2
12-4x11-0

Br 4
12-0x
10-0

Br 3
12-4x10-0

First Floor
1,395 sq. ft.

vaulted

Brk
11-0x
11-0

Kit
10-4x
11-8

Up

Family
14-3x18-0

P

R

W
D

storage

MBr
14-0x15-0

Dn

Foyer

sloped clg

Dining
12-4x11-4

Garage
21-4x21-0

40'-0"

Porch

59'-8"

Radcliffe

Rustic Stone Enhances Front Entrance

2,024 total square feet of living area

Special features

- Impressive fireplace and sloped ceiling in the family room
- Master bedroom features a vaulted ceiling, separate dressing room and a walk-in closet
- Breakfast area includes a work desk and accesses the deck
- 4 bedrooms, 2 1/2 baths, 2-car side entry garage
- Basement foundation

Price Code C

Pomona Park

Home Dedicated To Excellence

1,948 total square feet of living area

Special features

- Plans include designs for a shop or screened porch adjacent to the garage to best match your needs
- Handsome Floridian architecture with harmonious symmetry
- The breakfast room surrounded with windows is open to a vaulted great room with fireplace and a well-planned kitchen
- A glamorous master bath and two spacious walk-in closets are featured in the master bedroom
- 3 bedrooms, 2 1/2 baths, 2-car side entry garage with shop
- Basement foundation

Price Code C

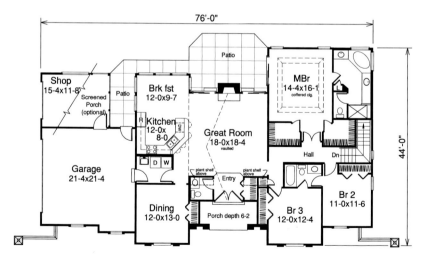

76'-0"

Patio

Shop 15-4x11-8

Screened Porch (optional)

Patio

Brk fst 12-0x9-7

MBr 14-4x16-1 coffered clg.

Kitchen 12-0x 8-0

Great Room 18-0x18-4 vaulted

Hall

Dn

44'-0"

Garage 21-4x21-4

D W

plant shelf above

plant shelf above

Entry

Dining 12-0x13-0

Porch depth 6-2

Br 3 12-0x12-4

Br 2 11-0x11-6

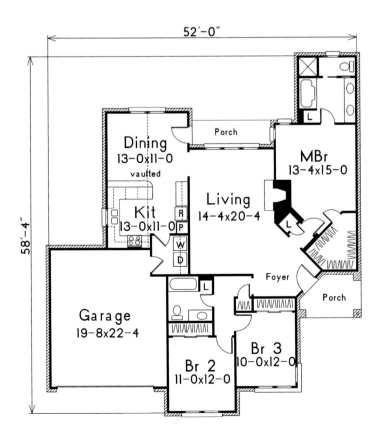

Winford

Sheltered Entrance Opens To Stylish Features

1,661 total square feet of living area

Special features

- Large open foyer with angled wall arrangement and high ceiling adds to spacious living room
- The kitchen and dining area have cathedral ceilings and a French door allowing access to the rear porch
- Utility room is conveniently located near the kitchen
- Secluded master bedroom has a large walk-in closet, unique brick wall arrangement and 10' ceiling
- 3 bedrooms, 2 baths, 2-car garage
- Slab foundation

Price Code B

Maybury

Stylish Master Bedroom Off By Itself

1,565 total square feet of living area

Special features

- Large vaulted great room with a full wall of glass opens onto the corner deck
- Loft balcony opens to rooms below and adds to the spacious feeling
- Bay-windowed kitchen with a cozy morning room
- Master bath features a platform tub, separate shower and a large walk-in closet
- 3 bedrooms, 2 1/2 baths, 2-car garage
- Basement foundation

Price Code B

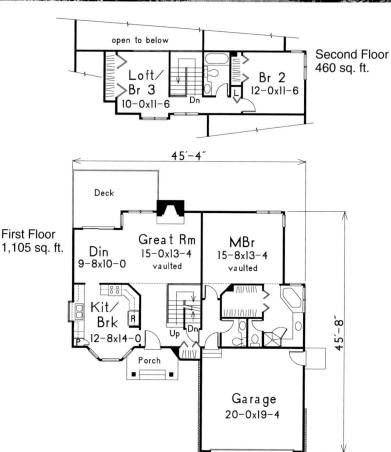

Second Floor 460 sq. ft.

Loft/ Br 3 10-0x11-6

Br 2 12-0x11-6

open to below

Dn

First Floor 1,105 sq. ft.

45'-4"

45'-8"

Deck

Din 9-8x10-0

Great Rm 15-0x13-4 vaulted

MBr 15-8x13-4 vaulted

Kit/ Brk 12-8x14-0

Up Dn

Porch

Garage 20-0x19-4

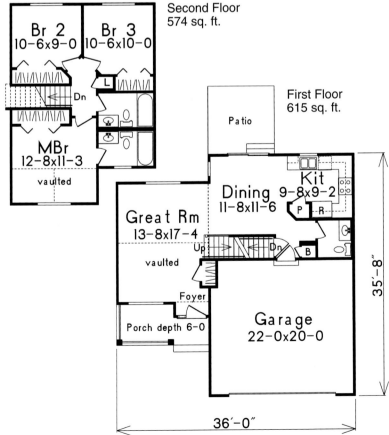

Second Floor
574 sq. ft.

Br 2
10-6x9-0

Br 3
10-6x10-0

L

Dn

MBr
12-8x11-3

vaulted

First Floor
615 sq. ft.

Patio

Kit
9-8x9-2

Dining
11-8x11-6

P R

Great Rm
13-8x17-4

Up Dn B

vaulted

Foyer

Porch depth 6-0

Garage
22-0x20-0

35'-8"

36'-0"

Concord

Spacious Vaulted Great Room

1,189 total square feet of living area

Special features
- All bedrooms are located on the second floor
- Dining room and kitchen both have views of the patio
- Convenient half bath is located near the kitchen
- Master bedroom has a private bath
- 3 bedrooms, 2 1/2 baths, 2-car garage
- Basement foundation

Price Code AA

Pepperwood

Sophisticated Efficiency

1,508 total square feet of living area

Special features

- Contemporary facade enhances appeal
- Vaulted ceilings and openness of living and dining rooms deliver spaciousness
- Kitchen has access to outdoors or an optional two-car garage
- Second floor bedrooms share a large bath with double-bowl vanity and skylight
- 4 bedrooms, 2 baths, optional 2-car garage
- Basement foundation, drawings also include crawl space and slab foundations

Price Code B

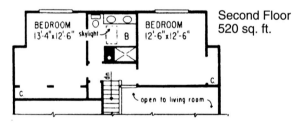

Second Floor
520 sq. ft.

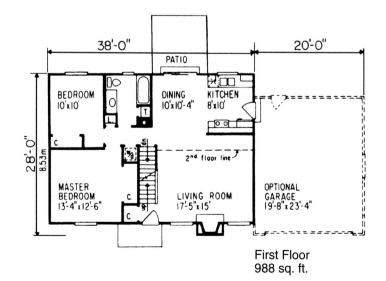

First Floor
988 sq. ft.

MBr
16-0x13-8

Br 3
12-4x10-0

Dn

open to
below

Br 2
12-4x12-7

Second Floor
952 sq. ft.

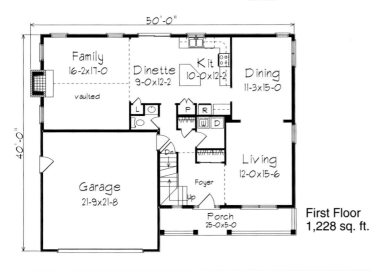

50'-0"

Family
16-2x17-0

vaulted

Dinette
9-0x12-2

Kit
10-0x12-2

Dining
11-3x15-0

40'-0"

L

P R

W D

Dn

Living
12-0x15-6

Garage
21-9x21-8

Foyer

Up

Porch
25-0x5-0

First Floor
1,228 sq. ft.

Elmswick

Excellent Design For Comfortable Living

2,180 total square feet of living area

Special features
- Energy efficient home with 2" x 6" exterior walls
- Informal dinette and formal dining area flank the kitchen
- The grand fireplace is the focal point in the vaulted family room
- Master bedroom includes bath with walk-in closet, shower and corner garden tub
- 3 bedrooms, 2 1/2 baths, 2-car garage
- Basement foundation

Price Code D

Brookdale

Formal And Informal Gathering Rooms

1,314 total square feet of living area

Special features

- U-shaped kitchen joins the cozy dining area
- The family room has direct access into the garage
- Roomy closets serve the second floor bedrooms
- 3 bedrooms, 1 1/2 baths, 2-car garage
- Basement foundation, drawings also include crawl space foundation

Price Code A

Second Floor
552 sq. ft.

Br 2
13-1x10-1

Dn

MBr
11-2x12-7

Br 3
9-10x9-3

First Floor
762 sq. ft.

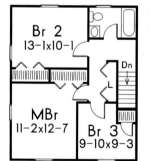

Dining
9-1x11-5

Kit
9-0x
11-5

Family
17-3x11-0

P R

Dn

Living
18-1x11-7

Up

Garage
19-8x20-0

32'-0"

Porch depth 6-0

42'-0"

156

To order this plan, visit the Menards Building Materials Desk.

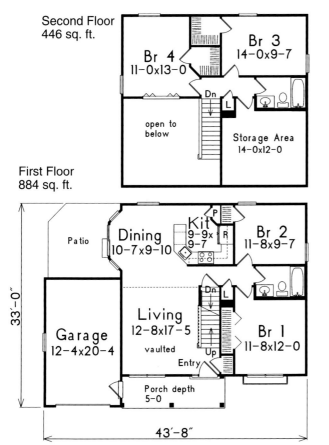

Second Floor
446 sq. ft.

Br 4
11-0x13-0

Br 3
14-0x9-7

Dn

L

open to
below

Storage Area
14-0x12-0

First Floor
884 sq. ft.

Patio

Dining
10-7x9-10

Kit
9-9x
9-7

P

R

Br 2
11-8x9-7

33'-0"

Dn

L

Garage
12-4x20-4

Living
12-8x17-5

vaulted

Up

Br 1
11-8x12-0

Entry

Porch depth
5-0

43'-8"

Tahoe

Openness Reflects Relaxed Lifestyle

1,330 total square feet of living area

Special features
- Vaulted living room is open to the bayed dining room and kitchen creating an ideal space for entertaining
- Two bedrooms, a bath and linen closet complete the first floor and are easily accessible
- The second floor offers two bedrooms with walk-in closets, a very large storage room and an opening with louvered doors which overlooks the living room
- 4 bedrooms, 2 baths, 1-car garage
- Basement foundation

Price Code A

Mountainview

Perfect For A Country Setting

1,293 total square feet of living area

Special features

- A very affordable ranch home that's easy to build
- Living room has separate entry, guest closet and opens to dining area
- Eat-in L-shaped kitchen offers pass-through to family room
- Master bedroom has its own bath and large walk-in closet
- 3 bedrooms, 2 baths, 1-car garage
- Basement foundation, drawings also include crawl space and slab foundations

Price Code A

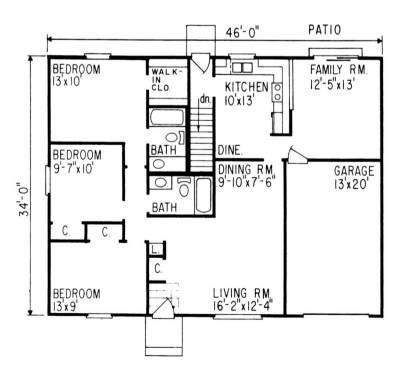

Second Floor
777 sq. ft.

Br 2
10-0x12-0

Br 3
10-0x12-0

Dn

L

MBr
15-1x11-3
Vaulted Clg.

48'-8"

30'-8"

Kit./Brk
20-1x10-10

Opt.
Sink

P

W

D

R

Garage
19-8x19-4

Dn

Family
18-9x13-8

Up

16x7 Gar. Door

First Floor
735 sq. ft.

Sunnytree

Delightful Family Home

1,512 total square feet of living area

Special features

- The spacious family room is warmed by a grand fireplace
- The kitchen/breakfast area features a pantry and access to the outdoors
- The laundry area includes space for an optional sink
- All bedrooms are located on the second floor for privacy
- 3 bedrooms, 2 1/2 baths, 2-car garage
- Basement foundation

Price Code B

Westley Manor

Cozy Ranch With Spacious Features

1,302 total square feet of living area

Special features

- The U-shaped kitchen features a snack bar, built-in pantry, open woodcrafted stairs to the basement and adjacent laundry/mud room
- Sliding doors to the patio and a fireplace with flanking windows adorn the vaulted family room
- The master bedroom accesses the patio through glass sliding doors and includes a private bath and walk-in closet
- 3 bedrooms, 2 baths, 2-car garage
- Basement foundation

Price Code A

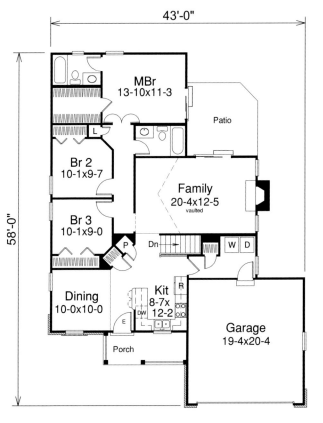

43'-0"

58'-0"

MBr
13-10x11-3

Patio

Br 2
10-1x9-7

Family
20-4x12-5
vaulted

Br 3
10-1x9-0

Dining
10-0x10-0

Kit
8-7x
12-2

Garage
19-4x20-4

Porch

160

To order this plan, visit the Menards Building Materials Desk.

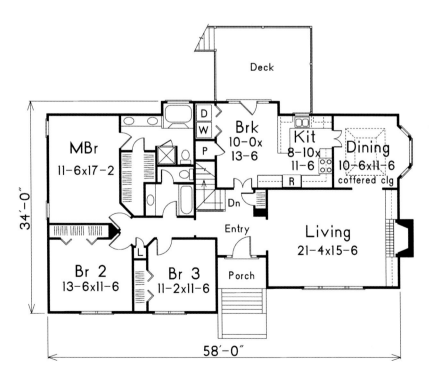

Glendale

Front Features Handsome Mullioned Windows

1,740 total square feet of living area

Special features

- The dining room boasts a coffered ceiling
- Master bedroom features a large bath with walk-in closet, double-vanity, separate shower and tub
- Both secondary bedrooms have ample closet space
- Large breakfast area is convenient to the laundry closet, pantry and rear deck
- 3 bedrooms, 2 baths, 2-car drive under garage
- Basement foundation

Price Code B

To order this plan, visit the Menards Building Materials Desk.

161

Arlington

Central Fireplace Warms Living Area

1,260 total square feet of living area

Special features

- Spacious kitchen and dining area features a large pantry, storage area and easy access to the garage and laundry room
- Pleasant covered front porch adds a practical touch
- Master bedroom with a private bath adjoins two other bedrooms, all with plenty of closet space
- 3 bedrooms, 2 baths, 2-car garage
- Basement foundation, drawings also include crawl space and slab foundations

Price Code A

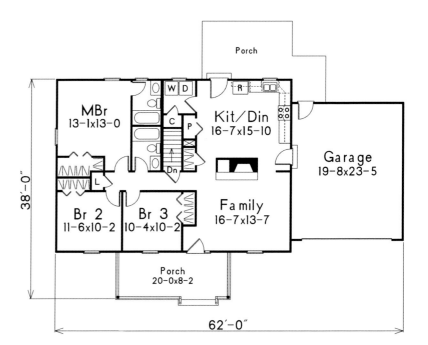

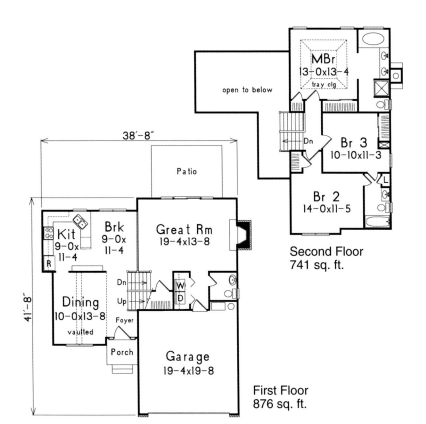

First Floor
876 sq. ft.

Second Floor
741 sq. ft.

Ridgeland

Efficient Layout In This Multi-Level Home

1,617 total square feet of living area

Special features

- Kitchen and breakfast area overlook the great room with fireplace
- Formal dining room features a vaulted ceiling and an elegant circle-top window
- All bedrooms are located on the second floor for privacy
- 3 bedrooms, 2 1/2 baths, 2-car garage
- Partial crawl space/slab foundation

Price Code B

MENARDS®

Chesnut Hill

Double Gables Create Appealing Facade

2,200 total square feet of living area

Special features

- Open first floor features convenient access to the laundry area
- Second floor captures space above garage for a large recreation area or future bedrooms
- Oversized country kitchen has plenty of space for entertaining
- Bonus room on the second floor is included in the square footage
- 3 bedrooms, 2 1/2 baths, 2-car garage
- Basement foundation

Price Code D

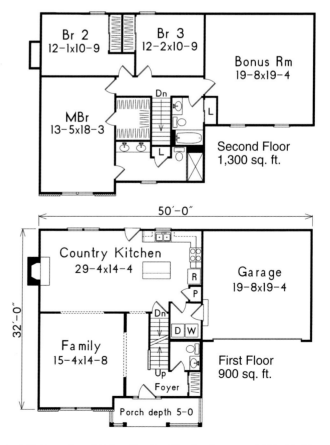

Second Floor
1,300 sq. ft.

Br 2
12-1x10-9

Br 3
12-2x10-9

Bonus Rm
19-8x19-4

MBr
13-5x18-3

Dn

L

L

L

50'-0"

32'-0"

Country Kitchen
29-4x14-4

R

P

Garage
19-8x19-4

Dn

D W

Family
15-4x14-8

Up

Foyer

Porch depth 5-0

First Floor
900 sq. ft.

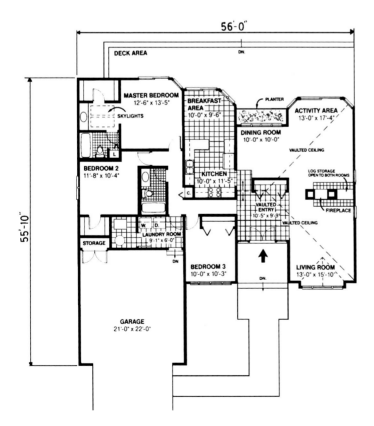

Imperial

Stylish Contemporary Living

1,850 total square feet of living area

Special features

- Living, dining and activity rooms have vaulted ceilings and share the warmth from an attractive see-through fireplace and log bin
- Well-equipped kitchen for mastering the culinary arts
- Master bedroom enjoys a compartmented bath with skylights and walk-in closet
- 3 bedrooms, 2 baths, 2-car garage
- Partial basement/crawl space foundation, drawings also include slab foundation

Price Code C

Hatteras II

Front Dormers Add Light And Space

1,705 total square feet of living area

Special features

■ Cozy design includes two bedrooms on the first floor and two bedrooms on the second floor for added privacy
■ L-shaped kitchen provides easy access to the dining room and the outdoors
■ Convenient first floor laundry area
■ 2" x 6" exterior walls available, please order plan #M02-001D-0111
■ 4 bedrooms, 2 baths
■ Crawl space foundation, drawings also include basement and slab foundations

Price Code B

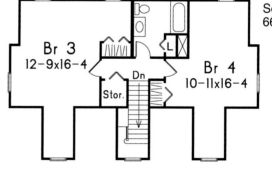

Second Floor
665 sq. ft.

Br 3
12-9x16-4

Br 4
10-11x16-4

Dn

Stor.

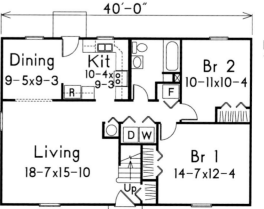

40'-0"

26'-0"

Dining
9-5x9-3

Kit
10-4x
9-3

Br 2
10-11x10-4

R

F

Living
18-7x15-10

D W

Br 1
14-7x12-4

Up

First Floor
1,040 sq. ft.

Pembrooke

Classic Styling With Framed Entry

1,739 total square feet of living area

Special features

- Utility room has convenient laundry sink
- Vaulted ceiling lends drama to the family room with fireplace and double French doors
- Island kitchen is enhanced by adjoining breakfast area with access to the patio
- Formal dining room features a 10' ceiling
- Private hallway separates the bedrooms from the living area
- 3 bedrooms, 2 baths, 2-car side entry garage
- Slab foundation

Price Code B

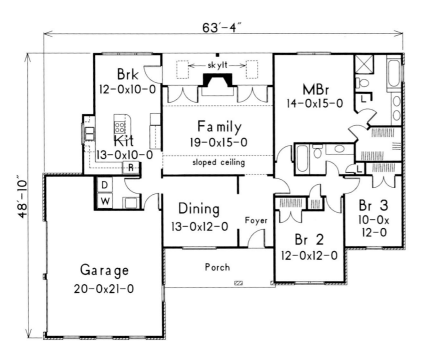

Floor plan dimensions: 63'-4" × 48'-10"

- Brk 12-0x10-0
- skylt
- MBr 14-0x15-0
- Kit 13-0x10-0
- Family 19-0x15-0 (sloped ceiling)
- Dining 13-0x12-0
- Foyer
- Br 3 10-0x 12-0
- Br 2 12-0x12-0
- Garage 20-0x21-0
- Porch

To order this plan, visit the Menards Building Materials Desk.

167

Cornwall

Embracing The Sun

1,850 total square feet of living area

Special features

- Large living room is illuminated by three second story skylights
- Living and dining rooms are separated by a low wall while the dining room and kitchen are separated by a snack bar creating a spacious atmosphere
- Master bedroom has a huge bath with double vanity and large walk-in closet
- Two second floor bedrooms share a uniquely designed bath with skylight
- 3 bedrooms, 2 1/2 baths, 2-car garage
- Basement foundation

Price Code C

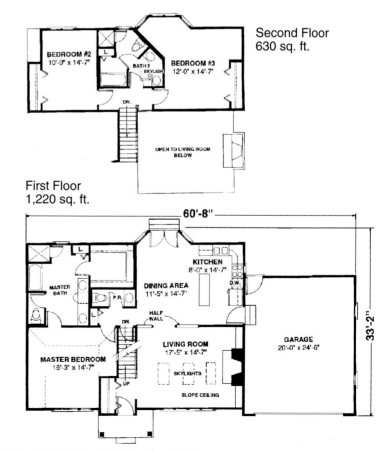

Second Floor
630 sq. ft.

First Floor
1,220 sq. ft.

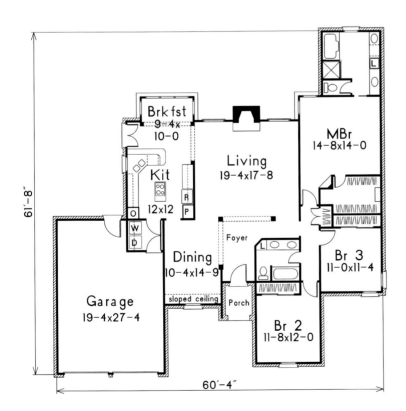

Ashwood

Stylish Features Enhance Open Living

1,846 total square feet of living area

Special features
- Enormous living area combines with the dining and breakfast rooms that are both complemented by extensive windows and high ceilings
- Oversized two-car garage has plenty of storage and workspace with handy access to the kitchen through the utility area
- Breakfast nook has wrap-around windows adding to enjoyment
- 3 bedrooms, 2 baths, 2-car garage
- Slab foundation

Price Code C

To order this plan, visit the Menards Building Materials Desk.

169

Westmont Manor

Cut-Above Features With A Classic Expression

2,154 total square feet of living area

Special features

- Open to the great room is a breakfast room surrounded by three 6' glass sliding doors that lead to the rear and side patios
- The kitchen features a long angled breakfast counter, and adjoins a multi-purpose room
- The vaulted master bedroom has a lavish bath, walk-in closets and adjoining study/nursery with an attractive bay window
- 4 bedrooms, 2 1/2 baths, 2-car side entry garage
- Basement foundation

Price Code C

64'-8"

Patio

MBr
14-1x14-5
vaulted

Brk fst
14-2x10-0
vaulted

Covered Patio

Great Room
18-5x18-0
vaulted

Kitchen
12-0x 12-9
vaulted

Study/Br 4
12-0x9-0

Multi-Purpose Room
10-0x11-3

Plant shelf above

Br 3
10-0x10-0

Entry

Dining
12-0x13-0

Dn   W D

tray clg.

Br 2
12-4x10-8

Porch

Garage
22-4x21-4

vault

55'-4"

170

To order this plan, visit the Menards Building Materials Desk.

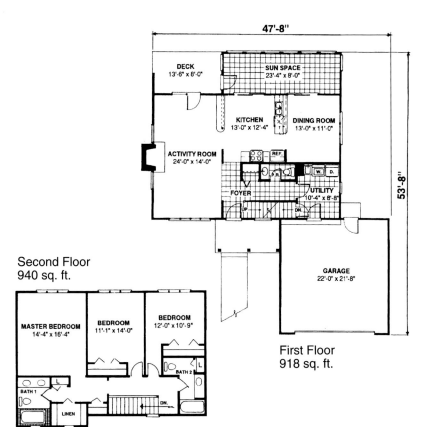

47'-8"

DECK
13'-6" x 8'-0"

SUN SPACE
23'-4" x 8'-0"

KITCHEN
13'-0" x 12'-4"

DINING ROOM
13'-0" x 11'-0"

ACTIVITY ROOM
24'-0" x 14'-0"

REF.

FOYER

UTILITY
10'-4" x 8'-8"

UP

DN.

53'-8"

W. D.

P.R.

GARAGE
22'-0" x 21'-8"

First Floor
918 sq. ft.

Second Floor
940 sq. ft.

MASTER BEDROOM
14'-4" x 16'-4"

BEDROOM
11'-1" x 14'-0"

BEDROOM
12'-0" x 10'-9"

BATH 2

BATH 1

LINEN

DN.

L

Grant

Distinctive And Charming Two-Level Living

1,858 total square feet of living area

Special features

- Huge activity room with fireplace receives welcome sunlight through lovely bay window
- Well-appointed kitchen enjoys pass-through counters to large dining and activity rooms
- Kitchen and dining room adjoin sun space that accesses deck
- Spacious utility room accesses garage, stair to basement and entrance foyer
- 3 bedrooms, 2 1/2 baths, 2-car garage
- Basement foundation

Price Code C

To order this plan, visit the Menards Building Materials Desk.

171

Woodland II

Unique
Split-Foyer Design

1,720 total square feet of living area

Special features
- Lower level includes large family room with laundry area and half bath
- L-shaped kitchen has a convenient serving bar and pass-through to dining area
- Private half bath in master bedroom
- 3 bedrooms, 1 full bath, 2 half baths, 2-car drive under garage
- Basement foundation

Price Code B

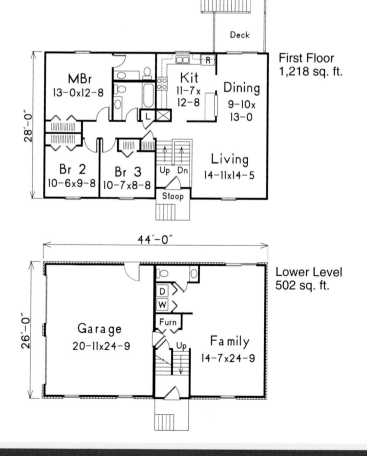

Deck

MBr
13-0x12-8

Kit
11-7x
12-8

Dining
9-10x
13-0

28'-0"

Br 2
10-6x9-8

Br 3
10-7x8-8

Up Dn

Living
14-11x14-5

Stoop

First Floor
1,218 sq. ft.

44'-0"

26'-0"

Garage
20-11x24-9

D
W
Furn

Up

Family
14-7x24-9

Lower Level
502 sq. ft.

First Floor
760 sq. ft.

35'-0"

Deck

Brk
3-0x
11-0

Kit
10-9x14-6

Dining
12-0x9-4

Living
15-8x14-0

Dn

Up

R

P

47'-8"

Porch

Garage
19-4x21-4

Second Floor
732 sq. ft.

MBr
11-0x14-8

Br 2
12-0x11-0

Dn

Br 3
12-0x9-9

raised
ceiling

Hampton

Home For Narrow Lot Offers Wide Open Spaces

1,492 total square feet of living area

Special features

- Cleverly angled entry spills into the living and dining rooms which share warmth from the fireplace flanked by arched windows
- Master bedroom includes a double-door entry, huge walk-in closet, shower and bath with picture window
- Stucco and dutch-hipped roofs add warmth and charm to facade
- 3 bedrooms, 2 1/2 baths, 2-car garage
- Basement foundation

Price Code A

Langham

Large Windows Grace This Split-Level Home

1,427 total square feet of living area

Special features

- Practical storage space is situated in the garage
- Convenient laundry closet is located on the lower level
- Kitchen and dining area both have sliding doors that access the deck
- Large expansive space is created by vaulted living and dining rooms
- 3 bedrooms, 2 baths, 2-car drive under garage
- Basement foundation

Price Code A

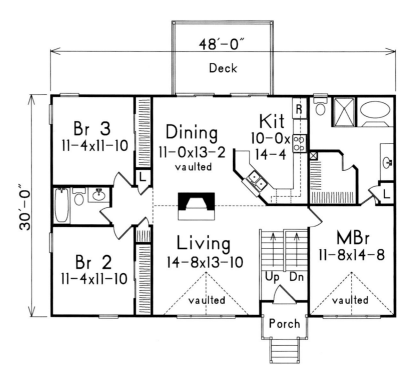

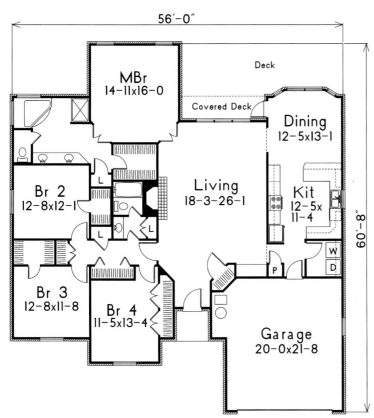

56'-0"

Deck

MBr
14-11x16-0

Covered Deck

Dining
12-5x13-1

Br 2
12-8x12-1

Living
18-3-26-1

Kit
12-5x
11-4

60'-8"

Br 3
12-8x11-8

Br 4
11-5x13-4

P

W
D

Garage
20-0x21-8

Quailcreek

Inviting Gabled Entry

2,128 total square feet of living area

Special features

- Versatile kitchen has plenty of space for entertaining with a large dining area and counter seating
- Luxurious master bedroom has a double-door entry and private bath with whirlpool tub, double sinks and large walk-in closet
- Secondary bedrooms include spacious walk-in closets
- Coat closet in front entry is a nice added feature
- 4 bedrooms, 2 baths, 2-car garage
- Slab foundation, drawings also include crawl space foundation

Price Code C

Wedgewood

Smaller Home Offers Stylish Exterior

1,700 total square feet of living area

Special features

- Two-story entry with T-stair is illuminated with a decorative oval window
- Skillfully designed U-shaped kitchen has a built-in pantry
- All bedrooms have generous closet storage and are common to a spacious hall with a walk-in cedar closet
- 4 bedrooms, 2 1/2 baths, 2-car side entry garage
- Basement foundation

Price Code B

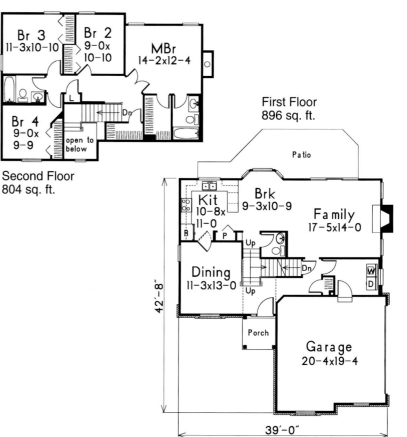

Br 3
11-3x10-10

Br 2
9-0x
10-10

MBr
14-2x12-4

Br 4
9-0x
9-9

open to below

L

Dn

Second Floor
804 sq. ft.

First Floor
896 sq. ft.

Patio

Kit
10-8x
11-0

Brk
9-3x10-9

Family
17-5x14-0

Dining
11-3x13-0

Up

P

Up

Dn

R

W
D

Porch

Garage
20-4x19-4

42'-8"

39'-0"

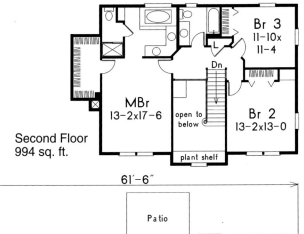

Second Floor
994 sq. ft.

Br 3
11-10x
11-4

L

Dn

MBr
13-2x17-6

open to below

Br 2
13-2x13-0

plant shelf

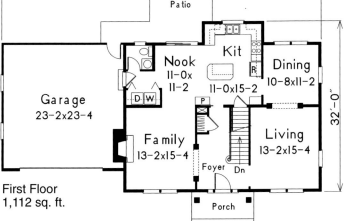

61'-6"

Patio

Garage
23-2x23-4

Nook
11-0x
11-2

Kit
11-0x15-2

Dining
10-8x11-2

DW

P

32'-0"

Family
13-2x15-4

Living
13-2x15-4

Foyer

Dn

Porch

First Floor
1,112 sq. ft.

Brunswick

Elegant Exterior

2,106 total square feet of living area

Special features
- Energy efficient home with 2" x 6" exterior walls
- Large two-story foyer features open staircase and plant ledge
- An arch with columns on either side separates dining and living rooms
- Master bath includes plush dressing area, double sinks, a spa tub, linen cabinet and a separate room with toilet and shower
- 9' ceilings throughout home
- 3 bedrooms, 2 1/2 baths, 2-car garage
- Basement foundation

Price Code C

Hillstone

Spacious Hillside Home

2,080 total square feet of living area

Special features

- The perfect design to accommodate a sloping site
- The generous great room features a vaulted ceiling, large bay window, fireplace and is open to the entry and dining areas
- For convenience, the kitchen is a U-shaped style and includes a garden window and built-in pantry
- The lower level offers a spacious family room, fourth bedroom, third bath, laundry and garage
- 4 bedrooms, 3 baths, 2-car drive under garage
- Basement foundation

Price Code C

First Floor
1,338 sq. ft.

Lower Level
742 sq. ft.

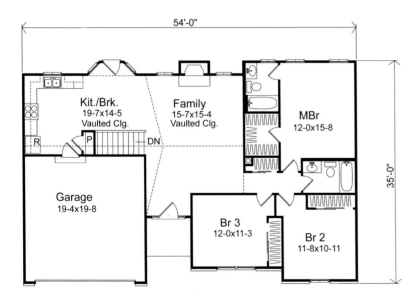

Amberidge

Cozy Bayed Breakfast Area

1,323 total square feet of living area

Special features

- The vaulted family room provides an elegant first impression
- The master bedroom enjoys a walk-in closet and private bath
- The kitchen connects to the breakfast area which includes access to the outdoors
- 3 bedrooms, 2 baths, 2-car garage
- Basement foundation

Price Code A

Richmond

A Trim Arrangement Of Living Areas

1,770 total square feet of living area

Special features

- Distinctive covered entrance leads into spacious foyer
- Oversized living room has a high ceiling and large windows that flank the fireplace
- Kitchen includes a pantry and large planning center
- Master bedroom has a high vaulted ceiling, deluxe bath, and private access outdoors
- 3 bedrooms, 2 baths, 2-car garage
- Slab foundation

Price Code B

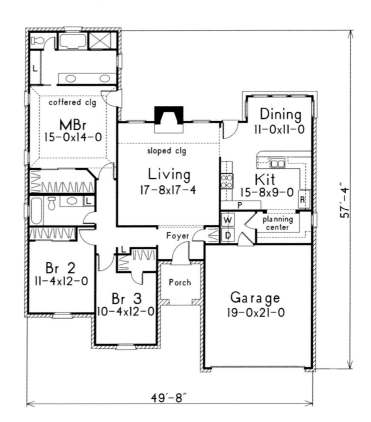

28'-0"

42'-0"

Br 1
11-8x11-0

MBr
12-8x11-0

Br 2
9-2x11-0

DN

Kit
10-6x14-4

R.

P.

Living
12-0x18-0

PORCH
5-8x4-0

Edison

Perfect Design For A Narrow Lot

1,112 total square feet of living area

Special features
- Energy efficient home with 2" x 6" exterior walls
- Brick, an arched window and planter box decorate the facade of this lovely ranch home
- The eat-in kitchen offers an abundance of counterspace and enjoys access to the outdoors
- Three bedrooms are situated together for easy family living
- 3 bedrooms, 1 bath
- Basement foundation

Price Code AA

To order this plan, visit the Menards Building Materials Desk.

181

Bradbury

Gabled Facade For A Lasting Impression

2,086 total square feet of living area

Special features

- Kitchen, breakfast nook, dining and activity rooms all have vaulted ceilings
- Skillfully designed kitchen features an angled island with breakfast bar
- Master bedroom is state-of-the-art with a luxury bath and giant walk-in closet
- 3 bedrooms, 2 baths, 2-car garage
- Partial basement/crawl space foundation

Price Code C

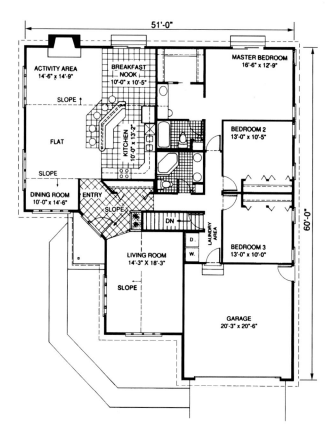

Savannah

Double Gables Frame Front Porch

1,832 total square feet of living area

Special features

- Distinctive master bedroom is enhanced by skylights, garden tub, and walk-in closet
- U-shaped kitchen features a convenient pantry, laundry area and full view to breakfast room
- Foyer opens into spacious living room
- Large front porch creates enjoyable outdoor living
- 2" x 6" exterior walls available, please order plan #M02-001D-0127
- 3 bedrooms, 2 baths, 2-car detached garage
- Crawl space foundation, drawings also include basement and slab foundations

Price Code C

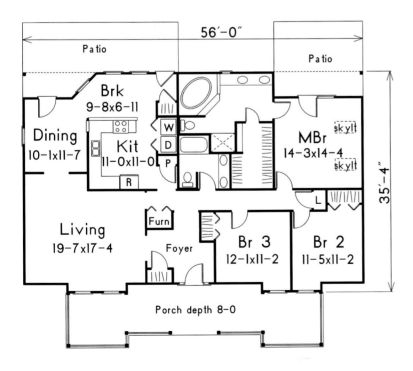

To order this plan, visit the Menards Building Materials Desk.

183

Brookview

Country Appeal For A Small Lot

1,299 total square feet of living area

Special features

- Large porch for enjoying relaxing evenings
- First floor master bedroom has a bay window, walk-in closet and roomy bath
- Two generous bedrooms with lots of closet space, a hall bath, linen closet and balcony overlook comprise the second floor
- 3 bedrooms, 2 1/2 baths
- Basement foundation

Price Code A

24'-0"

Patio

P
R

Kit
12-0x14-10

MBr
13-0x13-6

40'-0"

Dn

Living Rm
12-1x18-3

Up

L

L

Porch depth 6-0

First Floor
834 sq. ft.

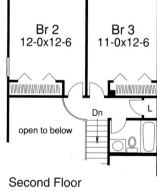

Br 2
12-0x12-6

Br 3
11-0x12-6

Dn

open to below

L

Second Floor
465 sq. ft.

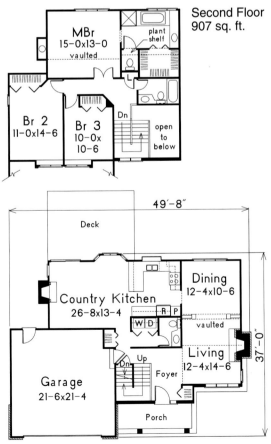

Second Floor
907 sq. ft.

MBr
15-0x13-0
vaulted

plant
shelf

Br 2
11-0x14-6

Br 3
10-0x
10-6

Dn

open
to
below

49'-8"

Deck

Country Kitchen
26-8x13-4

Dining
12-4x10-6

R P

W D

vaulted

Living
12-4x14-6

37'-0"

Up

Dn

Foyer

Garage
21-6x21-4

Porch

First Floor
928 sq. ft.

Lockport

Bright, Spacious And Appealing

1,835 total square feet of living area

Special features

- The arched entry and vaulted foyer create a welcoming appearance
- Divided dining and living rooms continue with vaulted ceilings to provide a distinguished openness
- Country kitchen with cozy fireplace and greenhouse windows offers a central gathering area
- All bedrooms are located on the second floor for added privacy
- 3 bedrooms, 2 1/2 baths, 2-car garage
- Basement foundation

Price Code C

Shelburne

Energy Efficient Home

1,536 total square feet of living area

Special features
- Formal living room featured in the front of the home
- Combined living areas create the back of the home with great room, dining area and kitchen all in one
- Second floor master bedroom includes a private bath
- 3 bedrooms, 2 1/2 baths, 1-car garage
- Basement foundation, drawings also include crawl space and slab foundations

Price Code B

Second Floor
768 sq. ft.

BED. RM.
11'-6"x11'

BED. RM.
11'-3"x10'

C.

C.   C.

dn

flue-
plan 2

BATH

MASTER BEDRM.
11'-6"x15'

BATH

First Floor
768 sq. ft.

24'-0"

DINE

opt. fireplace

bar

GREAT RM.
23'-3" x 12'-10"

ONE CAR 13'-8"

TWO CAR 21'-8"

32'-0"

dn.

GARAGE
13'-4"x21'-4"

LIVING RM.
11'-6" x 15'

up

storage

LAV

FOYER

C.

4'-0"

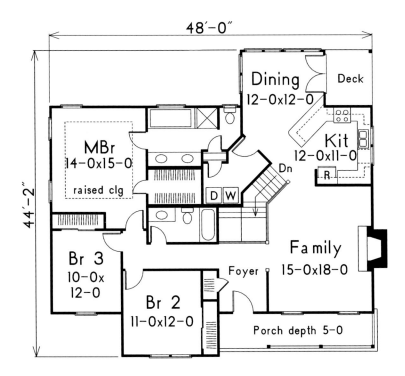

Bedford

Family Room With Fireplace Perfect For Central Gathering

1,631 total square feet of living area

Special features
- 9' ceilings throughout this home
- Utility room is conveniently located near the kitchen
- Roomy kitchen and dining area boast a breakfast bar and deck access
- A raised ceiling accents the master bedroom
- 3 bedrooms, 2 baths, 2-car drive under garage
- Basement foundation

Price Code B

To order this plan, visit the Menards Building Materials Desk.

187

Astoria

Handsome Facade, Compact Design

2,041 total square feet of living area

Special features

- Energy efficient home with 2" x 6" exterior walls
- Wonderful sunken family room features a fireplace and accesses the patio
- The kitchen with island cooktop and nook combines with the family room creating an open area
- Dining room is accessible from the kitchen and vaulted living room
- Bedroom #4 could easily convert to a study or den
- 4 bedrooms, 3 baths, 2-car side entry garage
- Partial basement/slab foundation

Price Code C

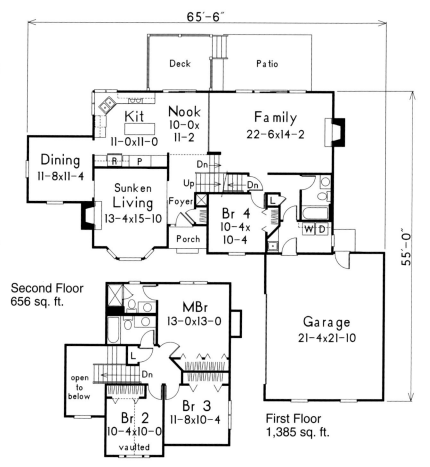

Second Floor
656 sq. ft.

First Floor
1,385 sq. ft.

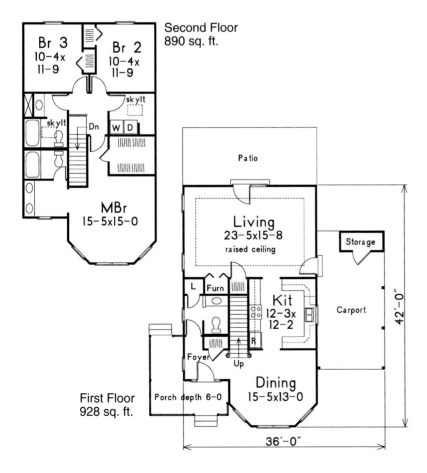

Second Floor
890 sq. ft.

Br 3
10-4x
11-9

Br 2
10-4x
11-9

skylt

skylt

Dn

W D

MBr
15-5x15-0

First Floor
928 sq. ft.

Patio

Living
23-5x15-8
raised ceiling

Storage

L Furn

Kit
12-3x
12-2

Carport

Foyer

Up

R

Porch depth 6-0

Dining
15-5x13-0

36'-0"

42'-0"

Covington

Large Bay Graces Dining Area And Master Bedroom

1,818 total square feet of living area

Special features

- Spacious living and dining rooms
- Master bedroom has a walk-in closet, dressing area and bath
- Convenient carport and storage area
- 2" x 6" exterior walls available, please order plan #M02-001D-0113
- 3 bedrooms, 2 1/2 baths, 1-car carport
- Crawl space foundation, drawings also include basement and slab foundations

Price Code C

Webster

Central Fireplace Dominates Living Area

1,444 total square feet of living area

Special features

- 11' ceilings in the living and dining rooms combine with a central fireplace to create a large open living area
- Both secondary bedrooms have large walk-in closets
- Large storage area in the garage is suitable for a workshop
- U-shaped kitchen includes a laundry closet and serving bar
- 3 bedrooms, 2 baths, 2-car side entry garage
- Slab foundation, drawings also include crawl space foundation

Price Code A

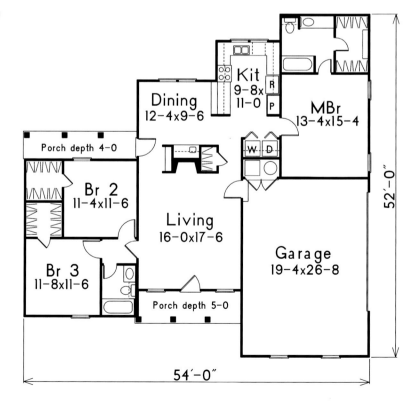

Porch depth 4-0

Dining 12-4x9-6

Kit 9-8x 11-0

MBr 13-4x15-4

Br 2 11-4x11-6

Living 16-0x17-6

Garage 19-4x26-8

Br 3 11-8x11-6

Porch depth 5-0

52'-0"

54'-0"

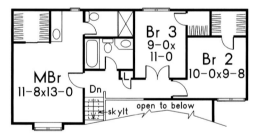

Second Floor
691 sq. ft.

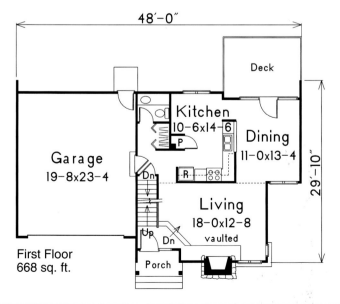

48'-0"

First Floor
668 sq. ft.

Walbrook

Exterior Accents Add Charm To This Compact Cottage

1,359 total square feet of living area

Special features

- Covered porch, stone chimney and abundant windows lend an outdoor appeal
- The spacious and bright kitchen has a pass-through to the formal dining room
- Large walk-in closets in all bedrooms
- Extensive deck expands dining and entertaining areas
- 3 bedrooms, 2 1/2 baths, 2-car garage
- Basement foundation

Price Code A

multi-family

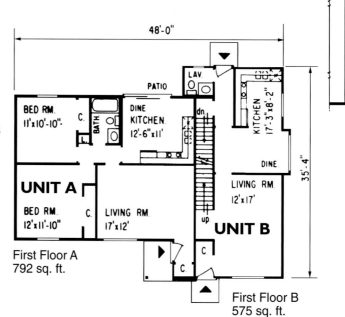

Monroe

Unique Duplex Style, Easily Fits In Neighborhood

1,924 total square feet of living area

Special features
■ Large bedrooms have plenty of closet space
■ Unit A features ranch-style living and has 792 total square feet of living area
■ Unit B is a 1 1/2 story and has 1,132 square feet of living area with 575 square feet on the first floor and 557 square feet on the second floor
■ Unit A has 2 bedrooms, 1 bath
■ Unit B has 2 bedrooms, 1 1/2 baths
■ Basement foundation

Price Code E

Second Floor
557 sq. ft.

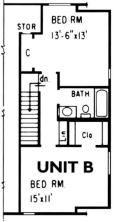

STOR

BED RM.
13'-6"x13'

C

BATH

Clo

UNIT B

BED RM.
15'x11'

48'-0"

PATIO

LAV.

BED RM.
11'x10'-10".

BATH

DINE
KITCHEN.
12'-6"x11'

dn.

KITCHEN
17'-3"x8'-2"

DINE

UNIT A

BED RM.
12'x11'-10"

C.

LIVING RM.
17'x12'

up.

LIVING RM.
12'x17'

UNIT B

C.

35'-4"

First Floor A
792 sq. ft.

C.

First Floor B
575 sq. ft.

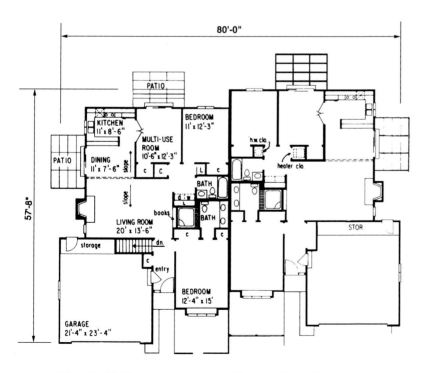

Plan 1 with Basement   Plan 2 without Basement

Pinedale

Open Floor Plan Is Perfect For Entertaining

2,662 total square feet of living area

Special features
- Living room has a vaulted ceiling, built-in bookshelves and a fireplace
- There is plenty of storage space in this duplex
- Large bedroom with a private bath and two closets is an ideal master suite
- Each unit has 2 bedrooms, 2 baths, 2-car garage
- Basement foundation, drawings also include crawl space/slab foundation
- Duplex has 1,331 square feet of living space per unit

Price Code G

multi-family

Newstead

Efficient And Open Duplex Design

896 total square feet of living area

Special features
- Small cabin duplex is well suited for rental property or permanent residence
- Compact, yet convenient floor plan
- Well organized for economical construction
- 2" x 6" exterior walls available, please order plan #M02-058D-0084
- 1 bedroom, 1 bath
- Slab foundation
- Duplex has 448 square feet of living space per unit

Price Code A

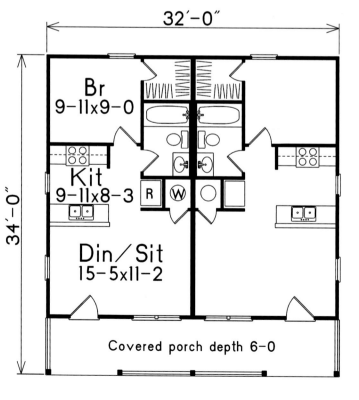

32'-0"

34'-0"

Br 9-11x9-0

Kit 9-11x8-3

R W

Din/Sit 15-5x11-2

Covered porch depth 6-0

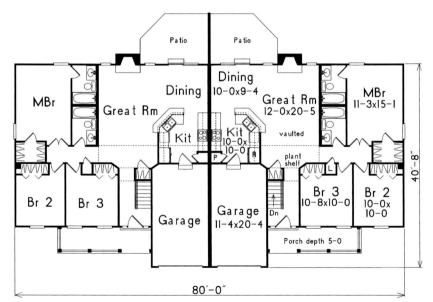

Shadydale

Vaulted Ceilings Add Spaciousness To Living Areas

2,318 total square feet of living area

Special features

- Great room and dining area are complemented with a fireplace and patio access
- Breakfast bar has a corner sink which overlooks the great room
- Plant shelf graces vaulted entry
- Master bedroom provides walk-in closet and private bath
- Each unit has 3 bedrooms, 2 baths, 1-car garage
- Basement foundation
- Duplex has 1,159 square feet of living space per unit

Price Code F

multi-family

Lakeside

Dutch Hips Create Attractive Facade

3,674 total square feet of living area

Special features

- Spacious second floor master bedroom has a large walk-in closet
- Kitchen has a snack counter which opens to the dining area and great room
- Each unit has 3 bedrooms, 2 1/2 baths, 2-car garage
- Basement foundation, drawings also include crawl space/slab foundation
- Duplex has 1,837 total square feet of living space per unit

Price Code H

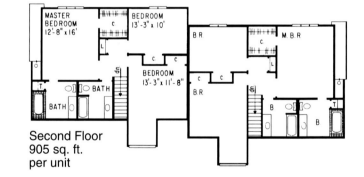

MASTER BEDROOM 12'-8" x 16'
BEDROOM 13'-3" x 10'
BEDROOM 13'-3" x 11'-8"
B.R.
M.B.R.
B.R.
BATH
BATH
B

Second Floor
905 sq. ft.
per unit

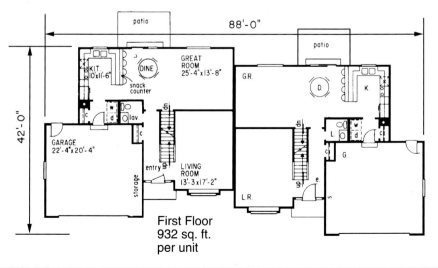

patio
88'-0"
patio
42'-0"
KIT. 10'x11'-6"
DINE
GREAT ROOM 25'-4"x13'-8"
G.R.
snack counter
D
K.
GARAGE 22'-4"x20'-4"
storage
entry
LIVING ROOM 13'-3x17'-2"
L.R.
G

First Floor
932 sq. ft.
per unit

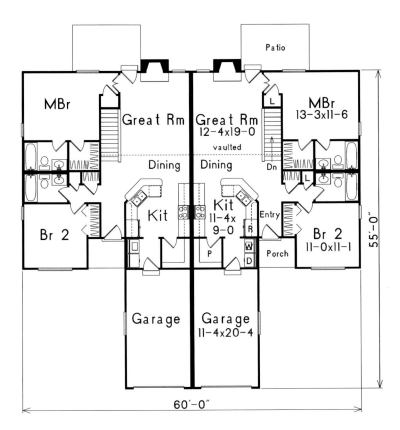

Highland

Stylish Living, Open Design

1,992 total square feet of living area

Special features

- Graciously designed ranch duplex with alluring openness
- Vaulted kitchen with accent on spaciousness features huge pantry, plenty of cabinets and convenient laundry room
- Master bedroom includes its own cozy bath and oversized walk-in closet
- Each unit has 2 bedrooms, 2 baths, 1-car garage
- Basement foundation
- Duplex has 996 square feet of living space per unit

Price Code E

To order this plan, visit the Menards Building Materials Desk.

197

multi-family

Ridgelane

Inviting Entry With Built-In Planter

1,966 total square feet of living area

Special features

- Energy efficient home with 2" x 6" exterior walls
- Entry opens into main living space or dining area/kitchen
- Ample closet/storage space throughout duplex
- Large L-shaped dining area/kitchen has garage access
- Several windows brighten living room
- Each unit has 2 bedrooms, 1 bath, 1-car garage
- Basement foundation
- Duplex has 983 square feet of living space per unit

Price Code E

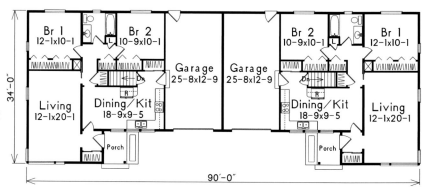

Second Floor
533 sq. ft.
per unit

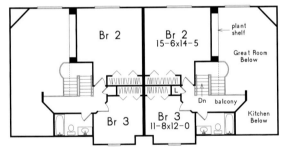

First Floor
960 sq. ft.
per unit

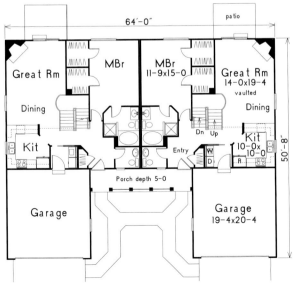

Countryridge

Country Charm In A Double Feature

2,986 total square feet of living area

Special features

- Vaulted great room, kitchen and two balconies define architectural drama
- First floor master bedroom boasts a lavish bath and double walk-in closets
- Impressive second floor features two large bedrooms, spacious closets, hall bath and balcony overlook
- Each unit has 3 bedrooms, 2 1/2 baths, 2-car garage
- Basement foundation
- Duplex has 1,493 square feet of living space per unit

Price Code G

multi-family

Coral Gables

Atrium Duplex With Room To Grow

3,666 total square feet of living area

Special features

- Inviting porch and foyer lead to the vaulted living room and dining balcony with atrium window wall
- Bedroom #2 doubles as a study with access to the deck through sliding glass doors
- Atrium opens to the large family room and third bedroom
- Each unit has 3 bedrooms, 2 baths, 2-car garage
- Walk-out basement foundation
- Duplex has 1,833 square feet of living space per unit

Price Code H

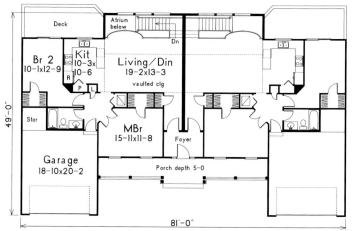

First Floor
1,073 sq. ft. per unit

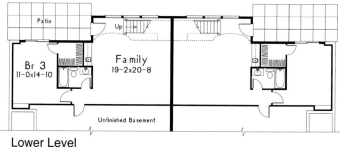

Lower Level
760 sq. ft. per unit

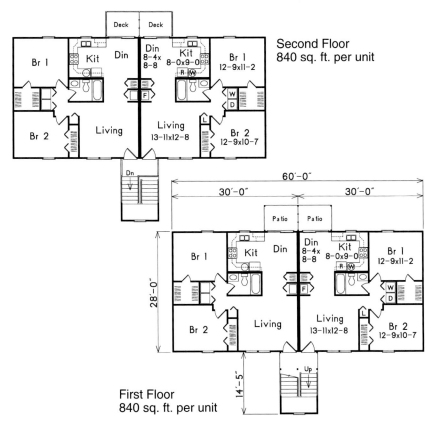

Second Floor
840 sq. ft. per unit

First Floor
840 sq. ft. per unit

Villager I

Spacious Layout For Comfortable Living

3,360 total square feet of living area

Special features

- Bedrooms have ample closet space
- Laundry closet is near both bedrooms
- Convenient U-shaped kitchen is adjacent to the dining room with access to the deck on the first floor and balcony on the second floor
- Each unit has 2 bedrooms, 1 bath
- Crawl space foundation, drawings also include slab foundation
- Fourplex has 840 square feet of living space per unit

Price Code H

To order this plan, visit the Menards Building Materials Desk.

201

MENARDS®

multi-family

Roseland

Covered Porch Entrance To Duplex

2,830 total square feet of living area

Special features

- Master bedroom features a double-door entry, walk-in closet and private bath with shower
- Laundry room with plenty of workspace conveniently accesses the outdoors, garage and kitchen
- 2" x 6" exterior walls available, please order plan #M02-058D-0071
- Each unit has 2 bedrooms, 2 baths, 2-car garage
- Basement foundation
- Duplex has 1,415 square feet of living space per unit

Price Code G

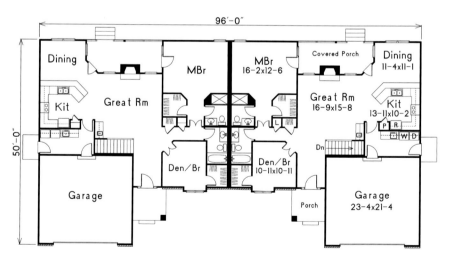

multi-family

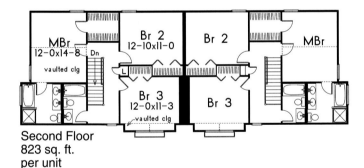

MBr
12-0x14-8

vaulted clg

Br 2
12-10x11-0

Br 2

MBr

Dn

L

Br 3
12-0x11-3

Br 3

vaulted clg

**Second Floor
823 sq. ft.
per unit**

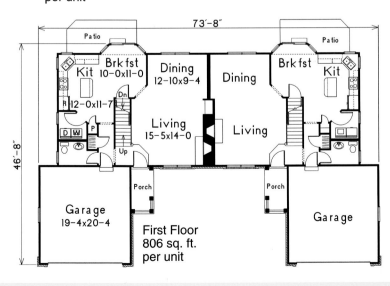

73'-8"

Patio

Patio

46'-8"

Kit
R 12-0x11-7

Brk fst
10-0x11-0

Dining
12-10x9-4

Dining

Brk fst

Kit

Dn

Living
15-5x14-0

Living

Up

D W P

Porch

Porch

Garage
19-4x20-4

**First Floor
806 sq. ft.
per unit**

Garage

Ashley Place

Traditional Elegance In A Duplex

3,258 total square feet of living area

Special features

- Multi-gables, brickwork, windows with shutters and planter boxes create great curb appeal
- Well-equipped kitchen includes an island snack bar, bayed breakfast room, built-in pantry, corner windows and laundry room
- Second floor has large bedrooms including a vaulted master bedroom with luxury bath
- Each unit has 3 bedrooms, 2 1/2 baths, 2-car garage
- Basement foundation
- Duplex has 1,629 square feet of living space per unit

Price Code H

multi-family

Weldon Pond

Cozy
Duplex Retreat

1,076 total square feet of living area

Special features

- A country porch for quiet times leads to a living room with fireplace, dining area and efficient kitchenette
- The bedroom offers a double-door entry, walk-in closet and a bath with linen closet
- Spacious and private screen porch is steps away from the dining area through sliding doors
- Each unit has 1 bedroom, 1 bath
- Crawl space foundation, drawings also include slab foundation
- Duplex has 538 square feet of living space per unit

Price Code B

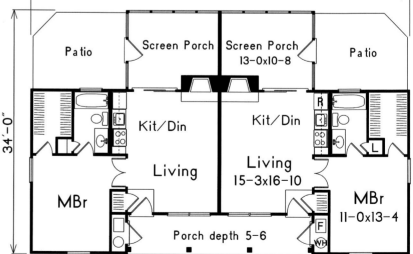

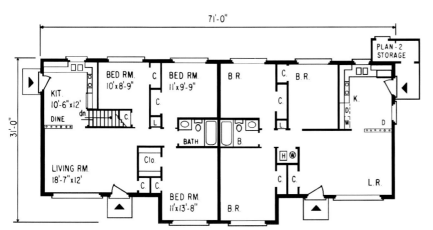

Plan 1 with Basement   Plan 2 without Basement

Hillcrest

Convenient And Open Floor Plan

1,966 total square feet of living area

Special features

- Lots of storage space throughout
- Oversized kitchen is easy to organize
- Large living room windows allow plenty of sunlight
- Each unit has 3 bedrooms, 1 bath
- Basement foundation, drawings also include crawl space/slab foundation
- Duplex has 983 square feet of living space per unit

Price Code E

multi-family

788

Shadywood Manor

A Fourplex With Distinction

2,986 total square feet of living area

Special features

- First floor units have access to sundecks while lower level units each enjoy a private patio
- Each unit features a hookup for a stacked washer and dryer
- Units A and B have 2 bedrooms, 1 bath and Units C and D have 1 bedroom, 1 bath
- Walk-out basement foundation with centrally located storage area
- Fourplex has 1,574 square feet of living area on the first floor and 1,412 square feet of living area on the lower level

Price Code G

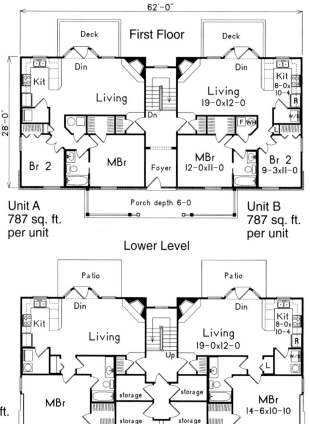

62'-0"

First Floor

Deck | Deck

Din | Din

Kit | Kit 8-0x 10-4

Living | Living 19-0x12-0

F WH

28'-0"

Br 2 | MBr | Foyer | MBr 12-0x11-0 | Br 2 9-3x11-0

Porch depth 6-0

Unit A 787 sq. ft. per unit

Unit B 787 sq. ft. per unit

Lower Level

Patio | Patio

Din | Din

Kit | Kit 8-0x 10-4

Living | Living 19-0x12-0

Up

Unit C 706 sq. ft. per unit

MBr | storage | storage | MBr 14-6x10-10

storage | storage

Unit D 706 sq. ft. per unit

WELCOME 1391

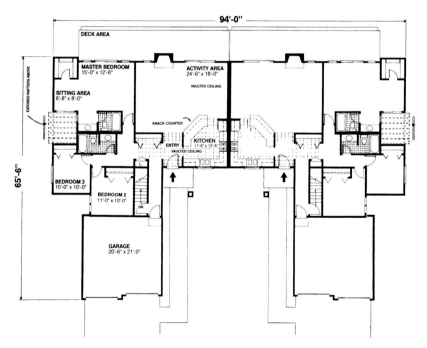

94'-0"

DECK AREA

MASTER BEDROOM
15'-0" x 12'-6"

ACTIVITY AREA
24'-6" x 18'-0"

VAULTED CEILING

SITTING AREA
6'-8" x 8'-0"

SNACK COUNTER

EXPOSED RAFTERS ABOVE

65'-6"

ENTRY

KITCHEN
11'-6" x 12'-6"

VAULTED CEILING

BEDROOM 3
10'-0" x 10'-0"

BEDROOM 2
11'-0" x 10'-0"

DN.

GARAGE
20'-6" x 21'-0"

Bradenton

Spacious Duplex With Luxurious Extras

3,066 total square feet of living area

Special features

- Master bedroom has a private bath, sitting area, walk-in closet and access outdoors
- Kitchen has a vaulted ceiling and a snack counter that overlooks the living room
- Roomy living room enjoys a fireplace, vaulted ceiling and access to deck
- Each unit has 3 bedrooms, 2 baths, 2-car garage
- Basement foundation
- Duplex has 1,533 square feet of living space per unit

Price Code G

To order this plan, visit the Menards Building Materials Desk.

207

multi-family

Meadowlane

Duplex With Cozy Front Porch

1,904 total square feet of living area

Special features

- Energy efficient home with 2" x 6" exterior walls
- Convenient laundry area and dining room are adjacent to the kitchen
- Garage has plenty of space for work/storage area
- Dining room features access to the outdoors
- Each unit has 2 bedrooms, 1 bath, 1-car garage
- Partial basement/crawl space foundation
- Duplex has 952 square feet of living space per unit

Price Code E

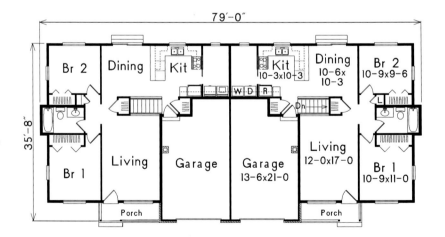

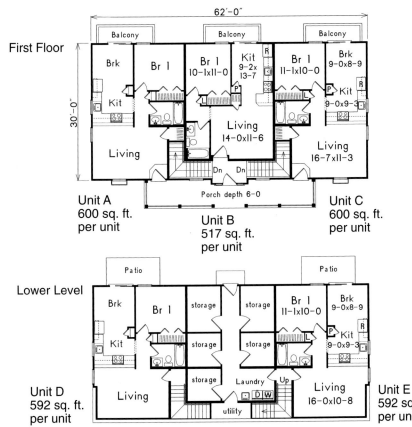

First Floor

62'-0"

30'-0"

Balcony | Balcony | Balcony

Brk | Br l | Br l 10-1x11-0 | Kit 9-2x 13-7 | Br l 11-1x10-0 | Brk 9-0x8-9

Kit

Living 14-0x11-6

Living | Living 16-7x11-3

Kit 9-0x9-3

Dn | Dn

Porch depth 6-0

Unit A
600 sq. ft.
per unit

Unit B
517 sq. ft.
per unit

Unit C
600 sq. ft.
per unit

Lower Level

Patio | Patio

Brk | Br l | storage | storage | Br l 11-1x10-0 | Brk 9-0x8-9

Kit | storage | storage | Kit 9-0x9-3

storage

Living | storage | Laundry | Up | Living 16-0x10-8

utility | DW

Unit D
592 sq. ft.
per unit

Unit E
592 sq. ft.
per unit

Norwood Hills

Multi-Family With Residential Look

2,901 total square feet of living area

Special features

- This fiveplex home features a large porch and lovely roof dormers
- Each unit has 1 bedroom, 1 bath
- Walk-out basement foundation with centrally located storage and laundry room
- Units A and C each have 600 square feet of living area, Unit B has 517 square feet of living area and Units D and E each have 592 square feet of living area
- Fiveplex has 1,717 square feet of living area on the first floor and 1,184 square feet of living area on the lower level

Price Code G

multi-family

Salem II

Compact Home With Large Living Area

1,536 total square feet of living area

Special features

- Living room joins the kitchen/dining area for an open atmosphere
- L-shaped kitchen with outdoor access and convenient laundry area
- Linen and coat closet
- Welcoming front porch
- Each unit has 2 bedrooms, 1 bath
- Crawl space foundation, drawings also include slab foundation
- Duplex has 768 total square feet of living space per unit

Price Code D

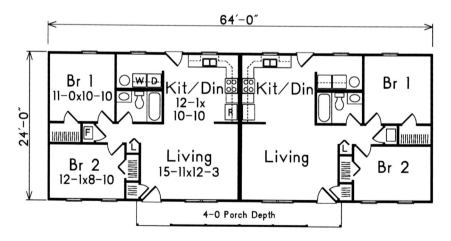

64'-0"

24'-0"

Br 1
11-0x10-10

W D

Kit/Din
12-1x
10-10

R

Kit/Din

Br 1

F

Br 2
12-1x8-10

L

Living
15-11x12-3

Living

L

Br 2

4-0 Porch Depth

210

To order this plan, visit the Menards Building Materials Desk.

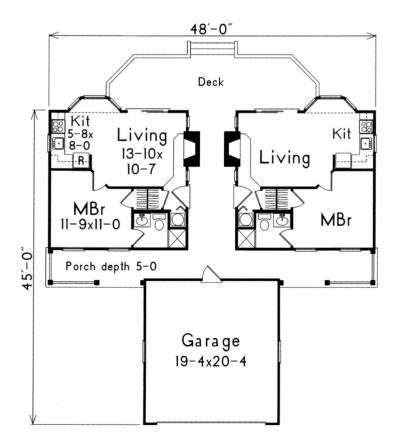

Cottage Grove

Double Cottage With Breezeway

844 total square feet of living area

Special features
- Unique design with maximum privacy for each unit featuring its own porch, breezeway entrance and large sundeck
- Living room offers separate entry with closet, fireplace, sliding doors to deck and opens to dining area with bay window
- The bedroom features a private bath, closet and views to porch
- Each unit has 1 bedroom, 1 bath and a shared 2-car garage
- Crawl space foundation
- Duplex has 422 square feet of living area

Price Code A

multi-family

Beacon Hill

Tudor Influences Enhance This Duplex

1,352 total square feet of living area

Special features
- See-through fireplace from the living room into the bedroom makes a lasting impression
- Covered front porch is perfect for relaxing evenings
- Galley-style kitchen is compact but well organized for efficiency
- Each unit has 1 bedroom, 1 bath
- Slab foundation
- Duplex has 676 square feet of living space per unit

Price Code C

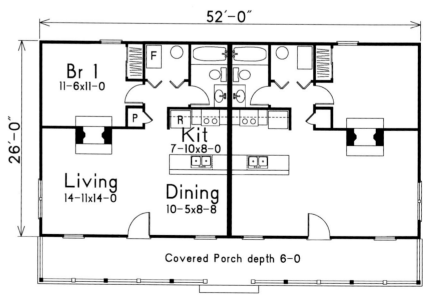

52'-0"

26'-0"

Br 1
11-6x11-0

Kit
7-10x8-0

Living
14-11x14-0

Dining
10-5x8-8

Covered Porch depth 6-0

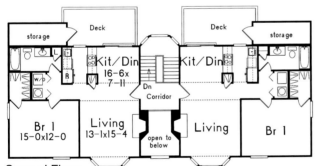

Second Floor
710 sq. ft. per unit

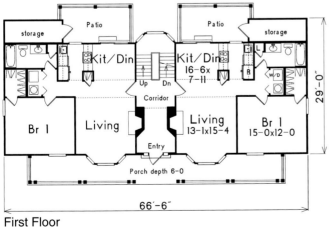

First Floor
710 sq. ft. per unit

Staunton

Fourplex With Southern Charm

2,840 total square feet of living area

Special features

- Living room is graced with a bay window and fireplace
- Kitchen offers efficient layout and overlooks dining area
- Bedroom includes a spacious walk-in closet
- Convenient laundry closet is located off hall
- First floor units have patios and second floor units have decks located off the dining area
- Each unit has 1 bedroom, 1 bath
- Basement foundation
- Fourplex has 710 square feet of living space per unit

Price Code G

multi-family

Harborview

Fourplex Is Spacious With Large Living Room

3,648 total square feet of living area

Special features

- The large kitchen is adjacent to the living room
- Handy linen closet in hallway
- Spacious living area has easy access to patio or balcony
- Centrally located laundry closet for stackable washer and dryer
- Each unit has 2 bedrooms, 1 bath
- Crawl space/slab foundation
- Fourplex has 912 square feet of living space per unit

Price Code H

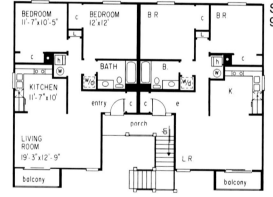

Second Floor
912 sq. ft. per unit

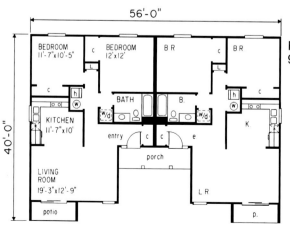

First Floor
912 sq. ft. per unit

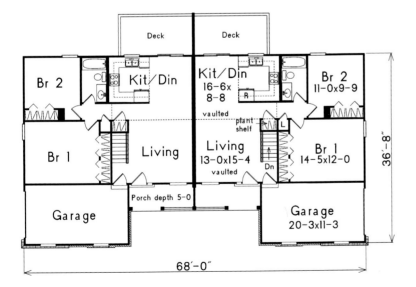

Brooktree

Duplex With Side Garage And Roomy Entry Porch

1,700 total square feet of living area

Special features

- Front facade fits splendidly with residential surroundings
- Well-planned kitchen includes an abundance of cabinets
- Spacious bedroom with double closets
- Convenient entrance from garage into main living area
- Dining room accesses deck
- Each unit has 2 bedrooms, 1 bath, 1-car side entry garage
- Basement foundation
- Duplex has 850 square feet of living space per unit

Price Code D

To order this plan, visit the Menards Building Materials Desk.

215

multi-family

Weston

Expansive, Open Space Created By Living Areas

2,800 total square feet of living area

Special features

- Energy efficient home with 2" x 6" exterior walls
- Large master bedroom enjoys a walk-in closet and private bath with linen area
- Work area in garage
- Convenient laundry room
- Half wall defines the kitchen and opens to the large living room
- Each unit has 2 bedrooms, 2 baths, 2-car garage
- Basement foundation
- Duplex has 1,400 square feet of living space per unit

Price Code G

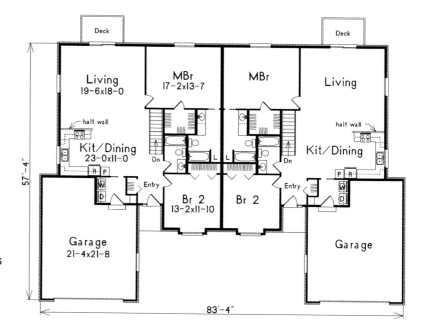

MENARDS®

Second Floor
1,558 sq. ft.

Mbr
11-6x18-0

Br #2
9-5x12-6

HALL

Br #3
13-8x11-7

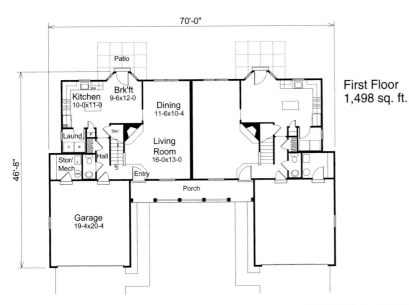

70'-0"

46'-8"

Patio

Kitchen
10-0x11-0

Brk'ft
9-6x12-0

Dining
11-6x10-4

Laund.

Stor.

Living
Room
16-0x13-0

Stor/
Mech

Hall

Entry

Porch

Garage
19-4x20-4

First Floor
1,498 sq. ft.

Hickory Manor

Traditional Two-Story Duplex

3,056 total square feet of living area

Special features

- Multiple gables, hipped roof and an elongated porch all help to create this handsome exterior
- A convenient laundry room, built-in pantry and island cabinetry are some of the many amenities of the well-equipped kitchen
- Each unit has 3 bedrooms, 2 1/2 baths, and a 2-car garage
- Crawl space foundation
- Each unit has 749 square feet on the first floor and 779 square feet on the second floor with 1,528 square feet of living space per unit

Price Code G

Jefferson

Outdoor Built-In Planters Add Style To This Duplex

2,010 total square feet of living area

Special features

■ Floor plan includes plenty of storage space

■ Cozy family room is adjacent to the kitchen and large living room

■ Both units have 2 bedrooms, 1 bath, 1-car garage

■ Basement foundation, drawings also include crawl space/slab foundation

■ Duplex has 1,005 square feet of living space per unit

Price Code E

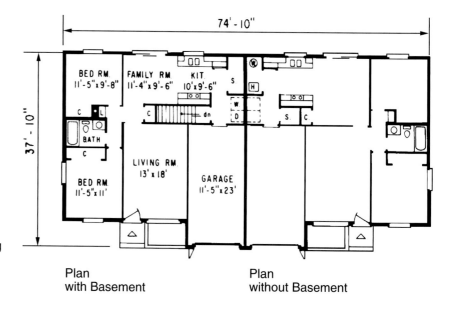

Plan with Basement

Plan without Basement

Salem I

Compact Home With Large Living Area

1,536 total square feet of living area

Special features

- Living room joins the kitchen/dining area for an open atmosphere
- L-shaped kitchen with outdoor access and convenient laundry area
- Linen and coat closet
- Each unit has 2 bedrooms, 1 bath
- Crawl space foundation, drawings also include slab foundation
- Duplex has 768 total square feet of living space per unit

Price Code D

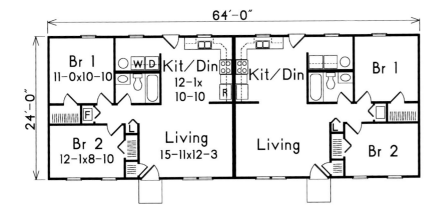

64'-0"

24'-0"

Br 1
11-0x10-10

W D

Kit/Din
12-1x
10-10

R

Kit/Din

Br 1

F

Br 2
12-1x8-10

Living
15-11x12-3

Living

Br 2

multi-family

Patterson Place

Compact Two-Story Duplex

2,408 total square feet of living area

Special features

- The large great room offers a fireplace and dining area with view of the patio
- Each unit enjoys its own private garage, front porch and rear patio
- The second floor bedrooms are large in size and feature spacious walk-in closets
- Each unit has 2 bedrooms, 1 1/2 baths, 1-car garage
- Basement foundation
- Duplex has 1,204 square feet of living space per unit

Price Code F

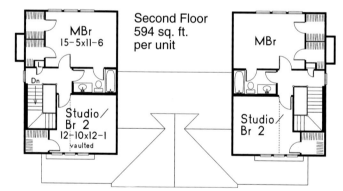

Second Floor
594 sq. ft.
per unit

MBr
15-5x11-6

Studio/
Br 2
12-10x12-1
vaulted

MBr

Studio/
Br 2

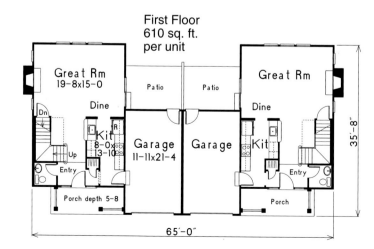

First Floor
610 sq. ft.
per unit

Great Rm
19-8x15-0

Dine

Kit
8-0x
13-10

Garage
11-11x21-4

Garage

Great Rm

Dine

Kit

Patio   Patio

Porch depth 5-8   Porch

35'-8"

65'-0"

Hickory Hill

Delightful Ranch Duplex

1,626 total square feet of living area

Special features

- Energy efficient home with 2" x 6" exterior walls
- Each unit features a lovely front porch that enters to find a coat closet and spacious living room
- The large eat-in kitchen offers plenty of space for dining and accesses the side yard
- The full bath includes a double-bowl vanity for ease of sharing
- Each unit has 2 bedrooms, 1 bath
- Slab foundation
- Duplex has 813 square feet of living space per unit

Price Code D

multi-family

Peppertree

Duplex With Plenty Of Style

1,704 total square feet of living area

Special features

- Smartly designed layout with emphasis on efficiency
- Functional kitchen embraces the sun with its bay window, glass sliding doors and pass-through to living room
- Five generously designed closets offer an abundance of storage
- Each unit has 2 bedrooms, 1 bath, 1-car garage
- Basement foundation
- Duplex has 852 square feet of living space per unit

Price Code D

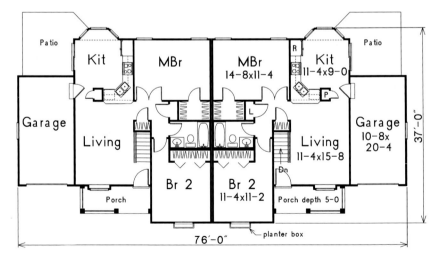

222

To order this plan, visit the Menards Building Materials Desk.

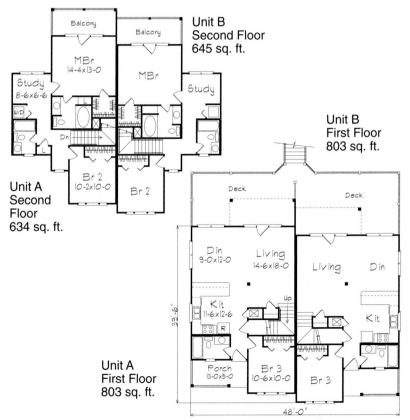

Unit A
Second
Floor
634 sq. ft.

Unit B
Second Floor
645 sq. ft.

Unit B
First Floor
803 sq. ft.

Unit A
First Floor
803 sq. ft.

Cottonwood

Elegant Exterior Accents Spacious Design

2,885 total square feet of living area

Special features

- Several windows brighten the main living area
- Practical counterspace in the kitchen overlooks the dining and living areas
- Convenient laundry closet is located on the second floor
- Each unit has 3 bedrooms, 3 baths
- Slab foundation
- Unit A has 1,437 square feet of living space and Unit B has 1,448 square feet of living space

Price Code G